# The State of the Art of Architecture
## *Guidebook*

CHICAGO
ARCHITECTURE
BIENNIAL

# CHICAGO ARCHITECTURE BIENNIAL

## The State of the Art of Architecture
*Guidebook*

October 3, 2015 – January 3, 2016

# CONTENTS

Bold: Alternative Scenarios
for Chicago

LAKEFRONT KIOSKS

STONY ISLAND ARTS BANK

WATER TOWER GALLERIES

OFF-SITE PROJECTS

GRAHAM FOUNDATION

A HISTORY OF CHICAGO
IN TEN ARCHITECTURES

Dear Friends:

As Mayor and on behalf of the City of Chicago, I am pleased to present the Chicago Architecture Biennial—the first international survey of contemporary architecture in North America.

In major cities across the globe—from Berlin to Beijing, from São Paulo to New York—politicians, architects, planners, and everyday citizens are discussing how to activate, revitalize, and improve urban environments. The Chicago Architecture Biennial's three-month exhibition and program of events showcases visionary ideas and projects by leading and emerging figures in the field, and is an incredibly important and timely endeavor that I am proud to launch, support, and host here in Chicago. The discourse, debates, and inspirations that it stirs will not only reverberate within Chicago's local communities, but also engage active participants in an ongoing dialogue that is taking place in major metropolises throughout the world.

Chicago's architecture is a celebrated part of our own local history and a vital part of the character of our city, but it is also a foundation of architectural history at large. Visitors from around the world come to Chicago to experience our buildings, parks, public spaces, and our incredible infrastructure. All of these aspects continue to stimulate a new generation of architects in Chicago who are shaping the future of our city. The Biennial welcomes architects from around the world to experience our cultural heritage, but also to interact with our community and to think about the space of our cities together. This is what architecture allows us to do.

I hope you enjoy this guidebook, as it presents an inside view of the architecture industry from around the world. I commend all the architects, photographers, and writers for your many contributions to this book, which captures some of the most beloved architecture in the world.

Sincerely,

Rahm Emanuel
*Mayor of Chicago*

# THE STATE OF THE ART OF ARCHITECTURE

There is no escaping the paradox of an exhibition of architecture. Its scale, its ubiquity, and its indispensability to everyday life make it seemingly impossible to view architecture from a critical distance, to observe it impartially, to capture even a small fraction of its material or spatial qualities within the walls of a building. Yet the founding of the Chicago Architecture Biennial, an institution launched by the City of Chicago and charged with bringing a major exhibition of architecture to the city every two years, is a forceful argument for the importance of such events today. The Biennial is a reminder that the limitless possibilities of architecture hold as much promise for the city today as they did 150 years ago, when Chicago first embraced its future as a prototype of urban modernity. The Biennial is the expression of the idea that such exhibitions are not only useful but necessary to the future of architecture, and are a critical resource not only for architects and designers, but also for the public and indeed other cities around the world.

The first Chicago Architecture Biennial borrows its title—"The State of the Art of Architecture"—from a 1977 conference organized by American architect Stanley Tigerman and hosted by the Graham Foundation in Chicago. Invited speakers included architects from New York, Chicago, and Los Angeles, who were to become some of the most influential practitioners and theorists in the following decades (among them Peter Eisenman, Frank Gehry, and John Hejduk). Each participant was asked to present a recent architectural project that illustrated a position on the state of architecture in the late twentieth century. In a similar spirit but with an expanded, global scope, the Biennial summons to Chicago a group of architects from around the world whose work tests the limits of the field, and with the expectation that the resulting diversity of projects and ideas will cast into doubt our certainties about what architecture is. Each participant is driven by a distinct set of hopes, preoccupations, ambitions, and ideologies, some of which converge, while others tug in opposing directions.

From the perspective of 1977, it would have been hard to predict the extraordinary degree to which the circulation of ideas and people was to accelerate in the following decades. The process of reciprocal influence is as ancient as architecture itself, yet its pace and geography have been fundamentally transformed in a brief period of time by the technological forces that define our era. Today we might take developments like the jetliner or the Internet for granted, but they have come to fundamentally shape the practice of architecture.

At the same time, new challenges of unprecedented complexity have thrust the importance of architecture back into the forefront of our collective consciousness, giving a new sense of relevance to the field and, demanding entirely different approaches to design. The vertiginous expansion of the world's urban footprint, the critical need for strategies to address environmental change, the persistent growth of inequality and social polarization: none of these are spatial questions alone, but none can be effectively addressed without design. These are precisely the questions the Biennial attempts to ask: what are the concerns, passions, and ambitions driving the work of architects today, and how do they reshape our understanding of architecture? What are the strategies being used to address these enduring challenges, and what dilemmas do architects face? How do architects employ creativity and ingenuity to tackle unanticipated crises and opportunities? What, in other words, is the agency of the architect?

In order to address such pivotal questions concerning the state of architecture at the beginning of the twenty-first century, we must cast a wide net. This exhibition is inclusive, with over one hundred invited participants from more than thirty countries. Accordingly, the themes and issues that the exhibited projects tackle create an incredibly broad range of ideas and forms of representation, which are outlined in this guidebook. For example, there is a sense of urgency in the research into new forms for the home that spans the work of practices from the United States to France, from Mexico to Vietnam. While urbanization is the primary concern for many participants, others have focused on strategies for rural regions. Others still engage political themes, experiment with new technology, and explore the realms of the imaginary. In the exhibition, visitors will find unconventional architectural ideas expressed through familiar media like models and drawings, in addition to an exceptional variety of photographs, objects, collages, performances, sculpture, and full-scale environments.

What unites all projects is the certainty that architecture matters, whether as a theoretical concern driving forward a collective dream or a concrete response to the questions of our time. Our aspiration is not to produce a unitary, systematic representation of architecture today; instead, we envisage the exhibition as a space for debate, dialogue, and the production of new ideas. It is our hope that this approach to the inaugural Biennial will be a useful foundation for its future editions, as well as the basis for a continuing conversation between the architectural profession and the public.

Few cities embraced the dream of modernity as wholeheartedly as Chicago, a place where the very notion of architecture as we understand it today was pioneered. There can be no better vantage point to consider what new opportunities will shape the future of the field over the decades to come. This exhibition is a round table at which people of all ages, backgrounds, and origins are invited to present their outlook on the state of the art of architecture. Like the city it is set in, the Biennial is an experiment in what is possible, an open invitation to contemplate what architecture is today, and what it can become tomorrow.

Joseph Grima, Sarah Herda
*Artistic Directors, first Chicago Architecture Biennial*

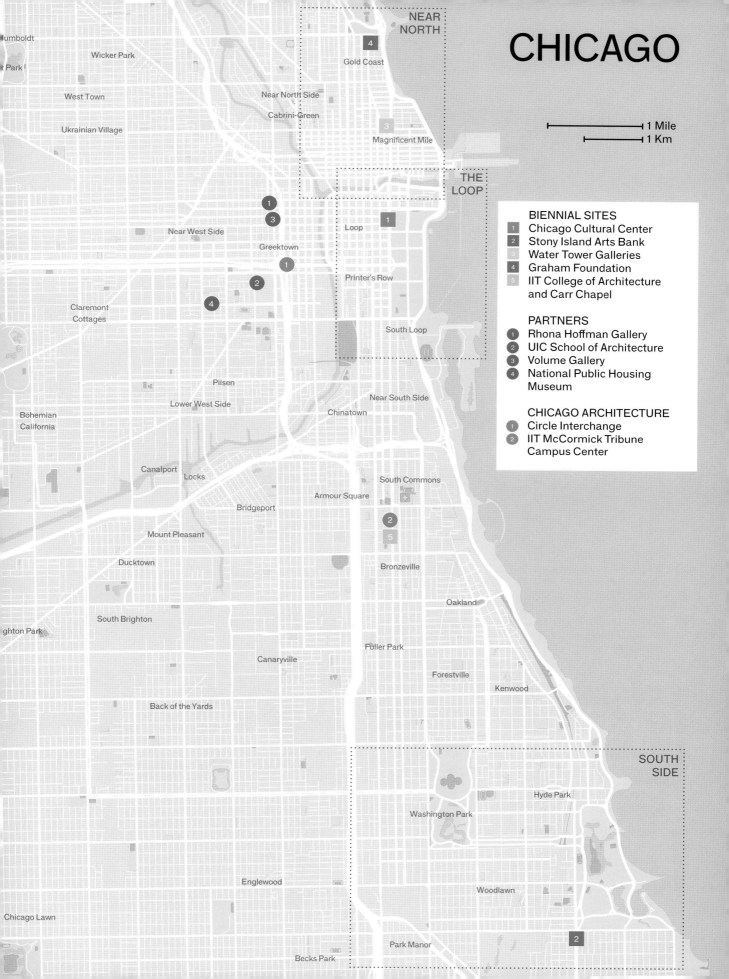

# CHICAGO

## BIENNIAL SITES
1. Chicago Cultural Center
2. Stony Island Arts Bank
3. Water Tower Galleries
4. Graham Foundation
5. IIT College of Architecture and Carr Chapel

## PARTNERS
1. Rhona Hoffman Gallery
2. UIC School of Architecture
3. Volume Gallery
4. National Public Housing Museum

## CHICAGO ARCHITECTURE
1. Circle Interchange
2. IIT McCormick Tribune Campus Center

1 Mile
1 Km

# THE LOOP

0.25 Mile

250 m

MILLENNIUM PARK

GRANT PARK

SOLDIER FIELD

**BIENNIAL SITES**
1. Chicago Cultural Center
2. Water Tower Galleries
3. Graham Foundation
4. Millennium Park
5. Queen's Landing
6. Chicago Federal Plaza
7. The Tank

**PARTNERS**
1. The Art Institute of Chicago
2. Chicago Architecture Foundation
3. Chicago Design Museum
4. Glass Curtain Gallery
5. Harold Washington Library
6. Harris Theater for Music and Dance
7. Museum of Contemporary Art Chicago
8. School of the Art Institute of Chicago

**CHICAGO ARCHITECTURE**
1. Auditorium Building
2. John Hancock Tower
3. Marina City
4. Monadnock Building

# SOUTH SIDE

0.5 Mile
500 m

**BIENNIAL SITES**
1 Stony Island Arts Bank

**PARTNERS**
1 Arts Incubator and Currency Exchange Café
2 DuSable Museum of African American History
3 Museum of Science and Industry
4 Rebuild Foundation (Dorchester Projects)
5 Rebuild Foundation (Black Cinema House)
6 The University of Chicago

**CHICAGO ARCHITECTURE**
1 The Robie House

East 54th Street
East 54th Street
East 54th Place
East 55th Street
East 55th Place
East 55th Street
East 56th Street
East 57th Dr
East 57th St
East 59th Street
East 60th Street
East 61st St
E 61st Pl
East 62nd Street
East 64th Street
East 65th Street
East 65th Place
East 66th Place
East 67th Street
East 67th Street
East 67th Street
East 68th Street
East 68th Street
East 68th St
East 69th Street
East 69th St
E. 69th Pl
East 70th Street
East 70th Street
East 70th Street

S. Ridgewood Court
S. Harper Avenue
South Blackstone Avenue
South Dorchester Avenue
South Cornell Avenue
South Hyde Park Boulevard
South Everett Avenue
South Shore Drive
South Lake Shore Drive
S. Shore Dr
South Lake Park Avenue
S. Harper Ave
South Blackstone Avenue
South Harper Avenue
South Stony Island Avenue
South Cornell Ave
South Lake Shore Drive
South Lake Shore Drive
S. Harper Ave
South Dorchester Avenue
South Blackstone Ave
S. Dorchester Ave
South Kenwood Avenue
S. Park Shore East Ct
South Cornell Ave
South Richards Drive
S. Promontory Dr
South Jeffery Boulevard
East Hayes Drive
East Hayes Drive
East Marquette Drive
East Marquette Drive

Osaka Garden
JACKSON PARK

S. Blackstone Ave
S. Dorchester Ave
South Dante Avenue
South Harper Avenue
South Stony Island Avenue
South Cornell Avenue
South East End Ave
South Ridgeland Avenue
South Cregier Avenue
South Constance Avenue
South Bennett Avenue
South Euclid Avenue
South Jeffery Boulevard
South Chappel Avenue
South Clyde Avenue
South Merrill Avenue
South Crandon Avenue
South Oglesby Avenue
South South Shore Drive

East Park Blvd
South Lake Shore Drive
ette Road
'd Street

1
4
5
3

CHICA

CULT
UR

The main hub of the Biennial is the Chicago Cultural Center, a five-story Beaux-Arts building opened in 1897, and located in the heart of downtown Chicago. Formerly home to the city's main public library, the building now functions as a thriving public institution. Frequently called the "People's Palace," it regularly hosts cultural events and exhibitions. The Chicago Architecture Biennial is the first time that the entire building is dedicated to a single curatorial project.

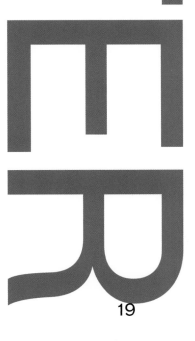

# AL BORDE
## *Quito, Ecuador*
## House under Construction

Photo: Raed Gindeya

Al Borde started *House under Construction* by looking for solutions to everyday problems. While the conventional market-driven formula applies generic solutions to specific problems, the firm's research aims to compensate for generic architecture with specific solutions.

*House under Construction* showcases the rehabilitation of an abandoned house in the historic center of Quito. The project aims to become a built manifesto, questioning our assumptions about architecture and the way we live, from economy and heritage to culture and society.

Al Borde brings its ideas to life through the design and construction of one stage of the *House.* The design process is broadcast online via daily updates on the firm's website.

*Project Team*

Pascual Gangontena, David Barragán, Malu Borja, Esteban Benavides, Maryangel Mesa, Carla Kienz, Hélène Thébault, Azul Castañeda, Elaine González, Antonio Flores, Luis Cadena, Juan Calderón, Adriana Ruíz, Melanie Kautz, Melanie Ponce, Oscar Soto, Flavia Burcatovsky, Céline Tcherkassky, Nicolás Ventroni, Simen Bie Malde, Florencia Sobrero, Charlotte Vaxelaire, Argenis Toyo

*Acknowledgements*

Christof Tononi & Dagmar Peñaherrera; Patricio Cevallos (structural engineering); Fabián Rojas (economic consulting); Jaime Erazo (economic consulting)

# ALL(ZONE)
## *Bangkok, Thailand*
# Light House: The Art of Living Lightly

All(zone)'s research is inspired by a context where architecture is lightweight—something more akin to furniture or utensils. Some traditional Thai houses are so light and flexible that they can easily be moved from one place to another; they make it possible to live in an environment saturated with light and air. The firm's research on the contemporary vernacular architecture of Thailand is the basis for an alternative modernism, one with a lower degree of rigidity and solidity.

*Light House* is a prototypical house for one person in the urban area of Bangkok (or any big tropical metropolis). It is composed of several layers of light, perforated walls, which create a living space of about 125 sq. ft. (11.5 m$^2$) with shared water facilities. The different degrees of transparency create variations within the space by selectively filtering external elements.

Recent housing projects in Bangkok are so closely tied up with global real estate investment that it is almost impossible for a young middle-class couple—not to mention a new generation of urban poor—to live in the city with what they earn. Furthermore, in ever-changing social and economic conditions, spending one's life savings on a house may not be such a safe investment anymore. As a result, many people are under pressure to adopt a more nomadic way of life.

At the same time, several modern high-rise buildings are left empty in the middle of the city, either unfinished from repeated financial busts or unoccupied because of obsolete building systems. These buildings are usually occupied by the homeless or by informal settlements.

*Light House* is an attempt to create a new type of domestic space in a tropical metropolis. Its half-temporary condition makes it ideal for inserting in an empty high-rise building. The structure can be quickly installed on any floor, and becomes a temporary urban-living unit to be dismantled and reassembled again in another site—just a bit larger than a suitcase.

*Project Team*
Rachaporn Choochuey, Sorawit Klaimark,
Ruchanan Patarapanich, Aroonrod Supreeyaporn,
Asrin Sanguanwongwan, Tanya Thapanand, Archaporn
Vashirasrisuntree, Weerachai Sirilorsakulpetch

*Acknowledgements*
Documentary film by Off Scene Films

# AMANDA WILLIAMS
## *Chicago, US*
## Color(ed) Theory

The *Color(ed) Theory* painted house series explores how academic and theoretical definitions of color map across the veiled language used in American media and popular culture to describe racially charged city spaces. What color is urban? What color is gentrification? What color is privilege? What color is poverty? Like a female Gordon Matta-Clark parading around as a Black Josef Albers in search of answers, Williams paints the exterior of abandoned houses on Chicago's South Side using a culturally coded, monochromatic color palette.

Colors are extracted from buildings and products that are frequent fixtures in Black American urban landscapes nationwide—currency exchanges, red Flamin' Hot Cheetos, Ultra Sheen grease. This project aims to become a system that imagines artful ways of constructing new narratives about zero-value landscapes, allowing such places to shed their identity of victimhood and instead embrace the role of protagonists.

With the painting of the final house of the series, the Chicago Architecture Biennial is the culmination of the *Color(ed) Theory* project.

*Project Team*
Amanda Williams, Siyu Guo, Sudeshna Sen

# ANDREAS ANGELIDAKIS
## *Athens, Greece / Oslo, Norway*
## Fantasy Ruins: Bags, Body Parts, and Bibelot

Andreas Angelidakis started making 3D prints in the early 2000s, as a way to keep a hard copy of buildings he had built in online virtual worlds, such as Active Worlds. The first world he designed was Chelsea in 1998, with artist Miltos Manetas. When they ran out of hosting space, all the buildings disappeared; they were built there, in what we now call the cloud, and they were all gone.

The first 3D prints were monochrome—white representations of the colorful online buildings. When Angelidakis exhibited the prints for the first time in 2003, one of them broke in transport. He showed it in its damaged state and called it a ruin. A ghost ruin.

As he gradually lost interest in online communities, selling off his last plot of land on Second Life, Angelidakis began to be interested in the prints as autonomous architectures—not a piece of memorabilia, not a ghost, but the final version of the building. At the same time, he decided to quit being a professional architect and just make these buildings. He did a farewell project called Domesticated Mountain, which was never meant to be built but was nonetheless represented with architectural drawings and models. From now on, models would be the originals. In Angelidakis's view, traditional architecture was losing any capability of newness; buildings that took years to complete were being consumed online in a matter of days, maybe hours.

As he continued to experiment with 3D printing, the results became more and more like ruins—buildings made of found objects, 3D scanned with an iPhone app, collaged with objects downloaded from 3D libraries. He played with the idea of *bibelot*, a French term invented for objects that have no clear use besides our potential emotional involvement in them. A bibelot can be an object of high or low value. A bibelot can be an object of exquisite or abominable taste.

He began to think of cities—Athens, in particular—as a collection of bibelot ruins, white elephants built for the Olympics and left to crumble. These were clearly commemorative objects, but they were also physical expressions of the crisis that Athens was sinking into.

The fantasy ruins became vehicles of escape. These buildings, collaged from objects collected on a beach, in a flea market, or on a website, are scaled according to their user: human clicks on social media, homes inhabited by "likes," tiny emojis. In fact, each of Angelidakis's buildings can be seen as an emoji, an abbreviated version of what is going on around him, rendered in architecture.

*Acknowledgments*
The Breeder Gallery, Athens

# ANNE LACATON & JEAN-PHILIPPE VASSAL + FRÉDÉRIC DRUOT
## *Paris, France*
## Imaginaries of Transformation

In 2004, Lacaton & Vassal and Frédéric Druot published *PLUS*, a manifesto in response to the French governmental policy of aggressive demolition and reconstruction of modernist public housing estates. After completing a similar project on the outskirts of Paris, they have been working, since 2011, on the transformation of 530 public housing apartments dating from the 1960s in the district of Grand Parc, Bordeaux. With a variety of improvements to both the interiors and the façades, and the addition of winter gardens and balconies, they enhanced the living conditions and energy efficiency of existing public housing—often portrayed as lacking in quality—at a fraction of the cost of demolition.

The Grand Parc project embodies the architects's proposal to plan cities from the inside out, starting from the domestic interior. The architects intend to work with the precision required at the urban scale, but with their feet on the ground. They start with one dwelling, then move on to another, paying the same amount of attention to each, regardless of whether this process needs to be repeated 500 or 500,000 times.

Many of the challenges that contemporary Western society faces stem from the continuous interpretation and transformation of what already exists—changing and optimizing a situation, rather than producing something new. Lacaton & Vassal and Druot oppose the current urban planning practices that burden cities with expensive large-scale plans and destroy existing resources through zoning and other simplistic strategies. Such attitudes undermine the potential of architecture as an open process and as a framework for liberty—one of the original tenets of modernism, which should be both advanced and questioned.

The film *Imaginaries of Transformation* shows an alternative future for public housing. The recurring images of the key phases of the construction process allow the firms to document the opening up of individual living spaces, the production of new geographies, and unexpected encounters. The film reveals the changes in the inhabitants' lifestyle after the renovation. While some evolutions and appropriations are obvious, others are completely unpredictable: no one knows in advance what will occur inside these apartments, or what will change.

*Project Team*
Anne Lacaton, Jean Philippe Vassal, Frédéric Druot (concept and curation); Philippe Ruault (photography, cinematography); Karine Dana (direction, mixing)

*Acknowledgements*
Christophe Hutin (associate architect for Grand Parc Project)

# ARANDA\LASCH
## *Tucson / New York City, US*
# Budidesa

*Budidesa*, located on the island of Bali, Indonesia, is a 161,000 sq. ft. (15,000 m$^2$) art foundation and park, containing gardens and exhibition spaces along with artist residences and visitor accommodation. The park is organized along a continuous circuit through nature and art that connects the site's collection of large-scale contemporary artwork. The project was conceived by Budi Tek, a Chinese-Indonesian collector dedicated to creating a new cultural destination in his homeland.

This project fits into the increasingly prevalent model of the art foundation as cultural destination—such as the island of Naoshima in Japan, and Inhotim in Brazil—where the type of work being displayed represents the predilections of an individual collector. In this case, Budi Tek's interests lie primarily in contemporary sculpture from both East Asian and Western artists. Not only does the work's scale create design constraints for its display both indoors and outdoors but its presence challenges the existing cultural milieu of Bali. What particularly charges Aranda\Lasch's project is the story of the landscape it will inhabit. Its surroundings are known as the Balinese Subak Cultural Landscape, portions of which are a UNESCO World Heritage Site. The foundation will sit in and under fields of rice paddies, in a landscape with a rich agrarian history of employing *Subak*.

Subak is the ancient water management system that nourishes the paddies as they step down the mountainside, one connected to another. Its cooperative nature warrants the system a profound social and, according to Balinese tradition, sacred dimension. Groups of farmers are organized in a network of local water temples where the annual rhythm of water distribution is tuned through a collective decision-making process. The Balinese Subak is a highly complex, self-organized interweaving of nature, agriculture, and tradition.

The inclusion of contemporary art into this landscape is charged with problems and opportunities. The problems lie in bringing non-indigenous art and its perceived value into a sensitive ecological area; but this is precisely the opportunity the project offers, showing how architectural and landscape design can help maintain the cultural identity of the Subak system while supporting a framework for the display of contemporary art. The project will give heightened visibility to the Subak as an evolving system capable of sustaining new forms of culture, in the face of rising pressure from a growing population and increasing tourism. Aranda\Lasch's ambition is to provide an alternative model for sustainable development and create a global art attraction that will be a lasting contribution to Balinese culture.

*Project Team*
Benjamin Aranda, Chris Lasch, Joaquin Bonifaz, Stephanie Lin, Alice Chai, Grace McEniry, Yoko Sara International (local architect)

# ARCHITECTEN DE VYLDER VINCK TAILLIEU
## *Ghent, Belgium*
## The Tennis Reenactment

In 2014, during the Porto Academy summer school, architects De Vylder Vinck Taillieu visited the Quinta da Conceiçao park in Porto, Portugal, which features a number of interventions by famed Portuguese architect Fernando Távora: small and large projects, a tennis court, a monumental entrance space, and several staircases.

While approaching the entrance space, the architects saw people playing tennis in the space and were told that this was a common occurrence. They wondered if the Távora-designed entrance was disturbed by this activity. Did the tennis players know what they were doing? Are we disrespectful if we dare to say that a new kind of beauty can be found in the eventual misuse of a masterpiece of architecture? What is the meaning of the art of architecture from an everyday perspective?

*The Tennis Reenactment* is a reflection on the friction between architectural ambitions and daily life. Following the experience at the Quinta da Conceiçao park, De Vylder Vinck Taillieu, together with the students of the Porto Academy summer school, set up a reenactment of tennis matches at a number of other buildings, starting with the Academy itself, which was designed by Álvaro Siza.

In the summer of 2015, they put out an open call, asking students from around the world to play tennis at an architectural landmark and submit a short film based on few simple guidelines (such as always shooting from the same angle). The resulting films have been collected and edited into a single piece, in which the simple action of playing tennis repositions architecture as a playful moment in daily life.

*Project Team*
Jan De Vylder, Inge Vinck, Jo Taillieu, Patricia Morais, Francisco Tavares, Max Kesteloot

*Acknowledgements*
Francisca Marques, Anamaria Miscu

# ASSEMBLE
## *London, UK*
## Baltic Street Adventure Playground

*Baltic Street Adventure Playground* is a key part of Assemble's ongoing work in the neighborhood of Dalmarnock, East Glasgow, Scotland. The playground project was developed in collaboration with the children and families of Dalmarnock.

*Baltic Street Adventure Playground* is child led and democratically managed. It offers free, open-access play, the attention of caring adults, daily campfire food, and warm and waterproof clothes to children from six to twelve years of age. Based on the understanding that, as author Hakim Bey put it, "cherishing and unleashing are the same act," Baltic Street offers space for children to grow in any and every direction they choose, embracing both creativity and destruction. Children are encouraged to self-organize, while workers maintain a secure, nurturing environment. The enviornment evolves in response to the children's growing needs, dreams, and capacity to affect change.

The Baltic Street project argues for the continued relevance of the adventure playground as a counterpoint to the pressures of modern urban childhood. Such places can be a refuge for a simple but radical set of ideas about childhood and our relationship to our immediate environment. *Baltic Street* was the flagship public art commission for the 2014 Commonwealth Games.

*Project Team*
James Binning, Lydia CS, Betsy Dadd, Amica Dall, Alice Edgerley, Fran Edgerley, Anthony Engi Meacock, Jane Hall, Joseph Halligan, Phineas Harper, Lewis Jones, Mat Leung, Maria Lisogorskaya, Louis Schulz, Giles Smith, Paloma Strelitz, Adam Willis

*Acknowledgements*
Baltic Street Adventure Playground, Clyde Gateway Development Corporation, Create, Creative Scotland, Glasgow City Council

# ATELIER BOW-WOW
## *Tokyo, Japan*
## Piranesi Circus

The courtyard of the Chicago Cultural Center is inaccessible, even though it is visible from all sides of the building. This relationship of secludedness enhances the perception of the courtyard as a void in the middle of the building. The proposition of bringing people into the courtyard presents several difficulties—not environmental or physical concerns but rather issues with security, safety, and facility management. In this sense, the void is actually a space governed by the functional rules of everyday life. The allegory behind G. B. Piranesi's *Carceri d'Invenzione* (*Imaginary Prisons*) could be recalled for this void space as a means to critique the constraints of daily life.

By introducing several suspended elements for movement and circulation, the courtyard is transformed into a marriage between an imaginary prison and a circus. A series of ramps, starting from the bottom of the courtyard, leads to one of the arched windows, with several benches along the way offering a privileged viewpoint from which visitors can look up and observe the scenario above.

A long ladder leaning against the western façade provides imaginary access to the roof. A suspended bridge visually extends the vertical path of the stairs out into the courtyard. As the immovable glass of the window negates access from within, the stairway continues further up, finding its way out to the roof. A cantilevered balcony extending from another window becomes an occasional point of access to a swing, suspended above the courtyard. The ramp, ladder, suspended bridge, cantilevered balcony, and swing are not accessible to the general public but are rather for the use of circus performers—or for imaginary prisoners.

*Project Team*
Yoshiharu Tsukamoto, Momoyo Kaijima, Yoichi Tamai, Hiroaki Goto, Simona Ferrari

*Acknowledgements*
Woodhouse Tinucci Architects

# BAUKUH + YELLOWOFFICE + STEFANO GRAZIANI
## Milan, Italy
## L'année dernière

Berlin is currently building a new forum of non-European cultures. The Humboldt Forum will be hosted inside a full-scale reproduction of the old Berliner Stadtschloss (City Palace), which, as a result, becomes a singular hybrid of progressivism (the content) and conservatism (the envelope).

In their entry for the 2013 competition to rebuild the Stadtschloss, Baukuh and YellowOffice chose to make visible, through the landscape, the multitude of contradictory desires incorporated into the Forum. The refined urban equilibrium that was disrupted with the demolition of the Palace in 1950 needed to be reactivated, yet the reconstruction should not erase its recent history.

The architects proposed surrounding the Forum with expansive Italian gardens. The gardens would produce a series of open spaces, composed of five groups defined by hedges of different species (both deciduous and evergreen) from all over the world. By filling the majority of the surfaces with intimate, low-intensity, or specialized functions such as restaurants, sport fields, or archaeological areas, what could have been experienced as an excessive quantity of public open space was reduced to a reasonable amount, producing three "squares" in front of the northern, western, and southern gates of the Forum.

The subdivision of the Italian gardens into smaller areas made it possible to satisfy the restrictions of the competition brief, turning them into opportunities and generators of form: paths leading to metro entrances and fire escape tracks contribute to the hybrid geometry of the gardens—half baroque, half futuristic.

The Italian gardens reestablish the link between the Palace, the Dom, and the Altes Museum. The proper distance between these landmarks is redefined, and the ancient gravitational system is reenacted. Yet while providing an efficient solution for the area, the Italian gardens produce a suspended, surreal tone. In an act of extreme realism, the gardens raise the question of their own legitimacy. Can this place in the middle of Berlin really be a new Arcadia?

*Project Team*
Francesca Benedetto, Antonio Buonsante, Nicola Campri, Paolo Carpi, Stefano Graziani, Jacopo Lamura, Silvia Lupi, Vittorio Pizzigoni, Giacomo Summa, Pier Paolo Tamburelli, Cecilia Tramontano, Mathias Winter, Andrea Zanderigo

*Acknowledgements*
Stefano Boeri, Paola Nicolin

# BESLER & SONS + ATLV
## *Los Angeles, US*
## The Entire Situation

Photos: Joshua White

No line has been drawn more clearly than the one dividing the discipline of architecture from the practice of building. While this has afforded architecture some critical distance from construction, it has established a gap that divides forms of intellectual work from forms of manual work. However, we no longer simply have architecture and building; today there are large systems of material distribution, supply chains, big-box retail, and bespoke fabrication. These networks surrounding construction have inhabited the architect's office for some time, smuggled in via product samples, material libraries, and mock-ups. Their imposition has never been more visible than it is today.

*The Entire Situation* is firmly positioned in this gap between disciplinary and practical problems. It repositions everyday aspects of construction that have been relegated to practice — namely the 1:1 architectural mock-up and Building Information Modeling (BIM) — into a conceptual framework.

One of the most ubiquitous architectural products available today is the steel stud. While seemingly straightforward, its use requires an order of expertise that sets the professional apart from the typical Do-It-Yourselfer.

Studs are not elements we are meant to see, buried inside the thickness of a wall and outside the purview of the architect. Architectural mock-ups, however, reveal their backside and expose those things that are often relegated to the realm of building. In *The Entire Situation*, Besler considers the stud not only within the domain of construction but also at the level of architectural finish and detail.

The mock-up holds a place in architectural practice as a specific type of model, one executed at 1:1 scale with "actual" building materials. Similarly, BIM sits in a curious position between conceptual and actual, where all geometry is represented as an architectural component. In a BIM model, a line is never simply a line; it is a Clark Dietrich 3⅝ in. 25-gauge steel stud, or a sheet of ½ in. Sheetrock UltraLight gypsum board, or a piece of ¾ in. American Pro molding.

Dismissing the mock-up and BIM as tools pertaining to the realm of practice rather than conception means overlooking the opportunity to rethink the relationship between architecture's digital and physical production today. The collision between architectural concepts and the practicalities of material use produces misalignments — literal gaps to enter.

*Project Team*
Jamie Barron, Erin Besler, Ian Besler, Sohun Kang, Jenny Rodenhouse, Satoru Sugihara, Evellyn Tan

*Acknowledgments*
BEHR

# BIG (BJARKE INGELS GROUP)
## *Copenhagen, Denmark*
## Steam Ring Generator

Image: BIG & MIR

By 2017, residents of Copenhagen will not only be able to ski down the cleanest power plant in the world, but their perceptions of what a power plant can be will be challenged by an art piece that raises awareness of carbon emissions. The world's first steam-ring generator will puff out a circle of steam for every ton of $CO_2$ produced by the plant as it burns the city's garbage. By openly projecting Copenhagen's carbon footprint onto the city's sky, BIG aims to help residents make informed decisions for their lives and encourages their participation in shaping the well-being of their city.

Based on an original art proposal by Berlin-based artists realities:united, the aerospace organization RaketMadsens Rumlaboratorium, and the Technical University of Denmark, BIG is designing the chimney that will make use of the plant's excess steam to generate steam rings. Work on chimney prototypes started in April 2014, and the project is expected to be completed in 2017. In the near future, if you come to Copenhagen and want to know how sustainable the city is, all you have to do is look at the sky and count the rings.

*Project Team*
Bjarke Ingels, Jakob Lange (BIG); Tim Edler, Jan Edler (realities:united); Peter Madsen (RaketMadsens Rumlaboratorium); Holger Koss (Civil Engineering and Architectural Aerodynamics, DTU); Jens C. Bennetsen (Ramboll – Advanced Flow Engineering)

# BUREAU SPECTACULAR
## *Los Angeles, US*
## Furniture Urbanism

In a domestic environment, the scattering of objects imposes order within a house. This type of urbanism creates micro-zones that we understand as programs—the kitchen, the bedroom, the living room, and so forth.

The dimensions, textures, shapes, figures, and postures perform another function—they give the room character, so that the inhabitants become players in a scene with a particular, identifiable sensation. The specificities of these orders depend on objectively measurable distances. This includes standards for sitting, standing, or lying down, and even the gaps between objects that inspire inhabitants to turn, stop, or continue. For example, the couch invites one to behave lazily in a cozy environment, preferably with more than one individual. Like a stage prop, objects signal the mood of the room. Moreover, they might indicate whether the territory is hostile, friendly, or calm.

*Furniture Urbanism* explores a lack of flexibility in an overly crowded environment. Rem Koolhaas's 1993 text "Typical Plan" was an exploration of the flexibility afforded by having very few permanent obstructions in modern office buildings. While the typical plan performs, in its flexibility, like an improvisational drama, furniture urbanism is akin to a script. In the project a hyperdense environment asks the question, is there value in a lack of flexibility, where there is nothing else to do except for what is in front of you?

*Project Team*
Jimenez Lai, Jacob Comerci

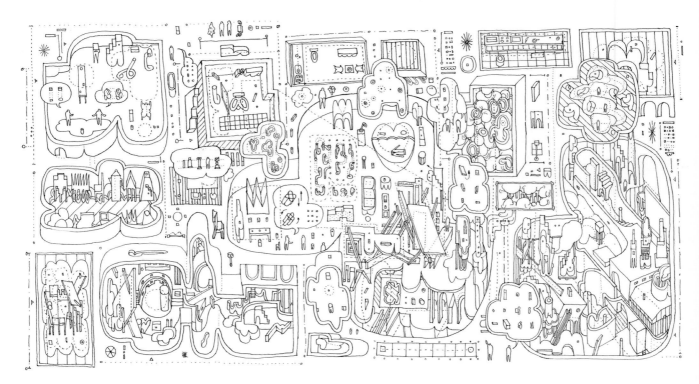

# COUNTERSPACE
## *Johannesburg, South Africa*
## Lost and Found: Phantoms of Spaces and Times

*Lost and Found* conveys the multiplicity of narratives that are legible in Johannesburg's landscape of mines. On a satellite map, a zoom-out view of the city shows yellow-and-white sand mountains—massive and imposing man-made nature scripted by subterranean gold—so vast that their monumentality lays bare the scale of exploitation by the colonial and apartheid regimes.

The minescape girdles the areas that belong to different racial groups, not only acting as a symbolic memory of political struggle but remaining a physical barrier between the various groups that were defined during apartheid.

A reversal of the lens—zooming in on the dust mountains —reveals architectures beyond the limits of formal planning and design. The mountains are sites of invisible cities. A face mask, an old rubber glove, and a makeshift pickax. A frosted-glass bottle with a label etched in Dutch script.

Plastic drive-in movie posters advertising a Valentine's Special. A Star-of-David badge, which has become host to a coral-like formation of turquoise crystals.

In *Lost and Found,* our minds fill in the stories contained in these mysterious artifacts. The narratives are constructed through real accounts, fictional text, maps, scientific readings, and photographs, blurring the boundary between physical place and imagined histories.

*Project Team*
Amina Kaskar, Sumayya Vally, Sarah de Villiers

*Acknowledgments*
Jason Larkin, Jaco van den Heever

# CSUTORAS & LIANDO
## *Jakarta, Indonesia*
## Misbar

In Jakarta there is a general shortage of public spaces and cultural venues outside of shopping malls, which compounds the segregation that characterizes Indonesian society. To watch a film, there are few other options than multiplex cinemas, which tend only to play current blockbusters.

On the occasion of the 2013 Jakarta Biennale, Csutoras & Liando teamed up with Kineforum, a nonprofit organization that screens art-house and independent movies, to create a temporary open-air cinema. The aim was to create a place to promote local movies that would be accessible to everyone, including those who cannot afford larger cinemas. Borrowing its name from the near-extinct, traditional, and inexpensive Indonesian open-air movie theaters, this became Kineforum *Misbar*.

The building was a simple structure, constructed using low-cost and reusable materials: a rented scaffolding system, plywood sheets, and agricultural netting. It consisted of a 150-seat cinema, separated from a generously sized foyer by a pavilion housing a ticket counter and a snack bar. It was located in the futsal area (a version of five-a-side soccer) of the large, popular park surrounding Monas, Indonesia's national monument.

Given the *Misbar*'s unique location, its relationship with its surroundings and with the people using the area became very important, informing the design of the façade to a great extent. The structure was wrapped in a large curtain made out of agricultural netting, which allowed wind to pass through, and made it possible for the films played at night to be watched from outside. A bench at the base of the façade turned out to be a popular and widely used feature—a place not just to watch the action on the neighboring soccer fields but also to lie down and rest, have a meal, or congregate with friends.

*Project Team*
Laszlo Csutoras, Melissa Liando

*Acknowledgements*
Sugar Nadia Azier/Kineforum, Sumarsono

# DAAR (DECOLONIZING ARCHITECTURE ART RESIDENCY)
## *Beit Sahour, Palestine*
## School in Exile

Photo: Sara Anna/Campus in Camps

Completed in August 2014 for the United Nations Relief and Works Agency (UNRWA) for Palestine Refugees in the Near East, the *School in Exile* consists of forty classrooms, a library, computer laboratory, a multipurpose room, a counseling room, and two administrative rooms, for use by 1,000 students, teachers, and local organizations.

What is exceptional about this school is its location—the Shu'fat refugee camp on the outskirts of Jerusalem. The camp was established in 1965 and is now inhabited by 20,000 Palestinians refugees who were expelled from fifty-five villages in the Jerusalem, Lydd, Jaffa, and Ramleh areas. It is enclosed by walls and fences that have been built by Israeli governments since 2002, which trap the inhabitants in a legal void, neither inside nor outside Jerusalem's borders, thereby making them vulnerable to losing their residency documents.

Is architectural intervention possible in such an unstable political environment? Too often within the humanitarian industry, architecture is reduced to answering the "needs of the community." Rarely is architecture used for its power to give form to social and political problems, and to challenge dominant narratives and assumptions.

The design of the school embodies an "architecture in exile." It is an attempt to inhabit and express the constant tension between the here-and-now, and the possibility of a different future. The architecture of the school does not communicate temporariness through an impermanent material construction. Rather, through its spatial and programmatic configuration, it attempts to actively engage the new "urban environment" created by almost seventy years of exile.

The design is inspired by the educational approach cultivated by Hilal and Petti in Campus in Camps, an experimental educational program based in the Dheisheh refugee camp in Bethlehem, Palestine. Their approach is devoted to the formation of egalitarian learning environments. The generative form of the School for Girls in Shu'fat is a hexagonal space in which all students are invited to participate equally in class discussions, whether in an indoor classroom or in the outdoor gardens.

*Project Team*
Sandi Hilal, Alessandro Petti, Livia Minoja

*Acknowledgements*
Campus in Camps, Bethlehem

CHICAGO CULTURAL CENTER

# DEANE SIMPSON
## *Copenhagen, Denmark*
## Young-Old: Urban Utopias of an Aging Society

The research project *Young-Old: Urban Utopias of an Aging Society* examines contemporary architectural and urban mutations that have emerged as a consequence of one of the key demographic transformations of our time: aging populations. Distinguishing between different phases of old age, Deane Simpson's project identifies the group known as the "young-old" as a remarkable petri dish for experiments in subjectivity, collectivity, and environment.

Through case studies, the project documents a range of socio-spatial phenomena rich in contradictions and paradoxes—from urban settings designed as micro-societies of youthfulness predicated on the elimination of youth, to forms of lifestyle urbanism constructed as "vacations that never end," which in fact generate new formats of work and "busy-ness."

*Young-Old* engages the range of opposing positions on these urban formats. It articulates young-old urbanism as a form of socio-spatial escapism, a conscious abandonment of wider societal contracts and responsibilities. This manifests itself, for example, in the tax-paying preferences of residents of age-qualified communities, who vote against contributing tax revenues to schools or maternity hospitals.

On the other hand, *Young-Old* introduces a new reading of these sites as radical urban experiments dedicated to the emancipation of the young-old from the traditional forms of marginalization associated with old-age—what urban historian Lewis Mumford called its "alienation, futility, and misery." In this context, the young-old may be framed as a group that has sought after or produced new environments supporting individual freedom and self-fulfillment, as well as new forms of collective life that resonate with some of the key utopian experiments of the twentieth century in unexpected ways.

Such a range of urban phenomena raises questions concerning the increasingly individualized, segmented, and aging societies in rich countries, where the institution of retirement and the demographics of the generational contract that support it face increasing pressure.

*Project Team*
Deane Simpson, Studio Joost Grootens (book and map design); Lars Müller Publishers, Ani Vihervaara (drawing and modeling assistance); BAS Kull 24 (modeling assistance)

*Acknowledgements*
Graham Foundation, Velux Foundation, Dreyers Foundation, Danish Arts Foundation, Holcim Foundation for Sustainable Construction, Husbanken Foundation , ETH-SEC Future Cities Laboratory

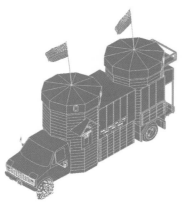

# DIDIER FAUSTINO
## *Paris, France / Lisbon, Portugal*
# BUILTHEFIGHT

[In Ancient Greek city-states] hoplitic weapons could not appear before a new social dispositif —the peasant-soldier who opposes the archaic form of the Greek army, that is to say a caste of warriors ... . The new dispositif of the peasant-soldier is a collective one ... . One of the most original hoplitic weapons is a simple tool: the shield with two handles ... . The shield with two handles is the best way to weld the soldiers to one another.
—Gilles Deleuze, *Le Pouvoir*, Lecture no. 12, 1986

In the wake of Occupy Wall Street and other similar protest movements that followed all over the world, Didier Faustino proposes a modular architecture that is designed to structure protest sit-ins.

*BUILTHEFIGHT* presents one assembled architecture composed of twelve modules. To be activated, the rough architecture requires a group of demonstrators who have gathered in the urban space. Each participant wears a device that links to those worn by others, to form an occupied territory.

Each ephemeral group will establish a compact and unmovable space. The aesthetic of the project also refers, paradoxically, to the design of anti-riot police equipment and chain-link fences. This duality places the demonstrator in a double condition: offensive and defensive. This prototype proposes a political "architecture-event," designed to enable defensive formations.

*Project Team*
Didier Faustino, Pascal Mazoyer, David Lévêque, Guillaume Viaud, Bérénice Serra, Emmanuelle Castella

*Acknowledgements*
Parque Galería, Mexico City; Institut Français

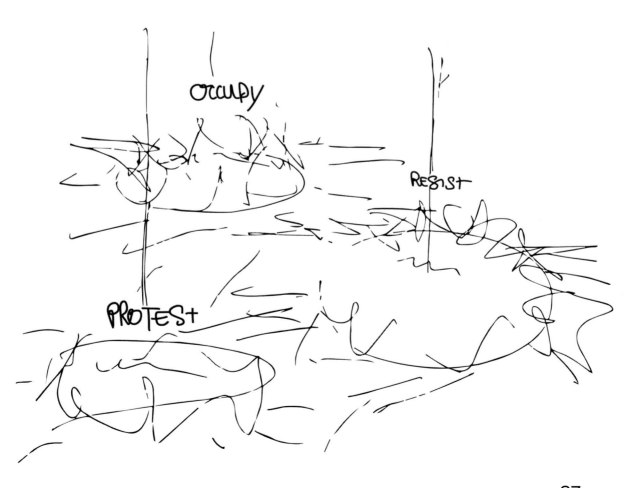

# EL EQUIPO DE MAZZANTI + NICOLAS PARÍS
## *Bogotá, Colombia*
## Speaking Architecture

What would happen if exhibitions were environments where architecture could learn to be an event? The most compelling exhibitions provoke more questions than they provide answers; they make people confront the unknown and recognize the limits of their own knowledge.

Taking this question as a premise, *Speaking Architecture* is conceived as a place to play, a canopy of actions and reactions, an architecture of events. The architects want to give visitors the opportunity to take control and create new architectures—new possibilities and different configurations of inhabiting space. The goal is to change the notion of habitation into an unstable, adaptable, or even mobile process that allows the emergence of new relationships and knowledge.

*Speaking Architecture* is not based on objects to be displayed (models, floor plans, renders). Rather, it is about building constellations—the relation between objects, events, and users. For this purpose, it adopts flexible tools such as drawing, model making, writing, dancing, resting, reading, assemble, and disassemble. Visitors' voices become the element that determines the architecture itself, letting them create their own plots.

Architecture can thus become a creative agent, open to the mental and physical contribution of its users. There is no program; only actions and movements that allow for unexpected forms of occupation and use.

*Project Team*
Giancarlo Mazzanti, Nicolas París, Carlos Medellín, Mariana Bravo, María Mazzanti

# FAKE INDUSTRIES
# ARCHITECTURAL AGONISM + UTS
## *New York, US / Sydney, Australia*
## Indo-Pacific Atlas

Photo: Jack Dunbar

The Indo-Pacific region extends from the east coast of Africa to the west coast of South America, including Southeast Asia and the Gulf. In 2013, the Australian Defence White Paper "Indo-Pacific Strategic Arc" officially relocated Australia at its center (previously, the country had belonged to the Pacific region). The government's claim, however, remains controversial in diplomatic circles. The Indo-Pacific region is an obvious attempt to displace an Atlantic vision of the globe, and Australia's aspiration to leadership sparks clashes with China as the region's center of gravity.

The *Indo-Pacific Atlas* consists of approximately 4,000 images that chart the intersections of media, capital flows, gentrification, and post-traumatic conditions as well as the discontinuities that these nodes have produced in recent urban history. The *Atlas* links Cape Town, Qatar, Valparaiso, and Medellín in a 33 ft. (10 m) long panorama, allowing visitors to navigate the relations between four parts of the project.

*Immaterial Company Town* chronicles the advent of mining towns that emerged from late-capitalist managerial logics. Examples include El Salvador in Atacama, Chile, the fly-in fly-out networks in Western Australia, and the recycling of outdated mining infrastructure in Valparaiso under the auspices of UNESCO.

*Die Antwoord's Gentrification* traces the connections between coexisting, yet apparently disconnected, forms of gentrification in Cape Town, such as the corporate redevelopment of the V&A Waterfront; the increasing hipster culture taking over Woodstock's graffiti, music, and homes; and the representation of *zef* culture in Die Antwoord's music videos.

*The Urbanism of Al Jazeera* explores the effects of postcolonial and distributed media on the representation of Middle Eastern cities: the emergence of Al Jazeera and its challenge to the Western portrayal of the Arab city; its aggressive expansion in East Africa and South America; and the role of social-media platforms in the Arab Spring.

*Medellín: A Tale of Two Cities* maps the urban policies in Medellín during and after the drug war of the 1980s and 1990s, and the overlapping urban interventions of drug lords and the municipality.

Developed by Fake Industries Architectural Agonism together with the researchers at MoRe, University of Technology Sydney, the *Indo-Pacific Atlas* challenges current accounts of the Indo-Pacific region that focus on informal urbanism and tabula rasa developments. Rather, it claims the intersection of civil society, public institutions, and private capital as the space for architecture to operate.

*Project Team*
Cristina Goberna, Urtzi Grau (Fake Industries Architectural Agonism); Miguel Rodríguez-Casellas (sound coordination); Endriana Audisho, Michelle Beck, Estelle Rehayem, Chrishani Thayaparan (Al Jazeera team); Kane Pham, Abulizi Alimujiang, Zoe Phocas Deliai, Hiaing Tun Oo, Natalie Xu (Cape Town team); Gonzalo Valiente, Faraneh Jabalameli, Shokoufeh, Rajaian, Qian Zhang, Melinda Barbagallo, Alice Zhaoying He (Company Towns team); Christina Deluchi, Kimberley Angangan, Marston Bowen, Liam Corr, Eduardus Intan (Medellín team)

*Acknowledgements*
Australian Consulate-General Chicago

# FALA ATELIER
## *Porto, Portugal*
## New Setubal Public Library

Decades of European Union–funded interventions in the site chosen for the library transformed it from an old romantic garden into a tabula rasa without references. The competition brief, launched in 2013, asked for a new public library. An "icon" was expected.

Fala Atelier's proposed building refuses any relation to the context: its circular floor plan and abstract monolithic appearance aim for an autonomous existence.

The first two floors are divided into four equal parts. The circulation area is located in the center of the circle, allowing for an efficient distribution of the program. All spaces are artificially illuminated and include occasional round windows for exterior views. The building's structural principles require no columns in the rooms, ensuring their versatility.

The reading room, the core part of the building program, takes over the entire third floor as a large pantheon with an endless bookshelf at its perimeter. This unique room's exterior shape reflects its grand interior space.

*Project Team*
Filipe Magalhães, Ana Luisa Soares

# GRAMAZIO KOHLER RESEARCH, ETH ZÜRICH + SELF-ASSEMBLY LAB, MIT
## *Zürich, Switzerland / Cambridge, US*
## Rock Print

*Rock Print* is a collaborative installation by Gramazio Kohler Research and the Self-Assembly Lab. It is the first architectural construction built by robotic machines using only rocks and thread, without any adhesive or mortar.

The project brings forward a new category of potentially random-packed, poly-disperse structures that can be automatically fabricated in nonstandard shapes. The resulting objects exhibit distinct features such as structurally active interlocking and differentiated structural performance, while yielding high geometric flexibility and articulation. Additionally, the transition from granularity to solidity is infinitely reversible, and the aggregated materials can be reused.

Featuring an impressive amount of rock in hitherto unseen and unexpected (digitally crafted) design configurations, the full-scale 3D rock-printing process uses the self-aggregating capacities of the material itself. While prevailing applications of jammed materials usually range from nano- to mesoscale, this newly created building system operates at a macroscale and is therefore suitable for architectural purposes.

By going far beyond the manual-assembly techniques of drystone walls, this project presents a unique combination of state-of-the-art knowledge from architecture, digital fabrication, and material science. It experiments with a new sustainable, economic, and structurally sound construction method in order to challenge the way architecture can be designed and built.

*Project Team*
Fabio Gramazio, Matthias Kohler, Skylar Tibbits, Andreas Thoma, Petrus Aejmelaeus-Lindström, Volker Helm, Sara Falcone, Lina Kara'in, George Varnavides, Stephane de Weck, Jan Willmann

*Experts*
Hans J. Herrmann, Falk K. Wittel (Institute for Building Materials, ETH Zürich); Heinrich Jaeger, Kieran Murphy (Chicago University)

*Consultants*
Walt + Galmarini AG

*Sponsors*
Pro Helvetia Swiss Arts Council, swissnex, MISAPOR Beton AG

# IWAN BAAN
## *Amsterdam, The Netherlands*

Iwan Baan's photographic work investigates architecture as a stage for everyday life, capturing the movements and encounters that shape the perception of buildings. His constant travel and relentless production embody the globalized state of architecture in the early twenty-first century.

A selection of new aerial images of Chicago show the city's key architectural landmarks set within the wider cityscape.

They emphasize Chicago's industrial landscape, reinforcing it as an ongoing center of production.

A second photographic project expands on the themes of industry and infrastructure. Here, Baan draws on Alvin Boyarsky's research on Chicago as an "energy system," shifting his perspective to (and below) street level.

# JOHN RONAN ARCHITECTS
*Chicago, US*
Leaf Lounge: Between
Building and City

The *Leaf Lounge* claims a small slice of space from the urban realm to become an outdoor lounge where visitors can retreat for relaxation and social engagement. Made of ordinary materials and employing an economy of means, the *Leaf Lounge* adds another layer to the Chicago Cultural Center and blurs the spatial distinction between building and city.

The lounge space is created through a temporary, L-shaped wall approximately 6 ft. (1.8 m) high. The wall is built of welded wire baskets filled with leaves fallen from local trees. Once the baskets are full, the wire structure fades from view and the wall appears to be made entirely of leaves.

The wall configuration responds to the Chicago grid, turning at a right angle to create two entrances—a wider, public approach near the Cultural Center's main entrance and a more discreet passage on the side street. The floor of the lounge is covered in a bed of leaves, enriching the aural and tactile experience, while tree stumps provide seating.

The *Leaf Lounge* is about relationships rather than form. It proposes a site- and culture-specific way of making architecture. It is designed to create a memorable experience and support meaningful human interaction between visitors coming from near and far.

*Project Team*
John Ronan, Eric Cheng, Marcin Szef, Sam Park,
Danielle Beaulieu, Laura Gomez Hernandez

# JOHNSTON MARKLEE
## *Los Angeles, US*
## House Is a House Is a House Is a House Is a House

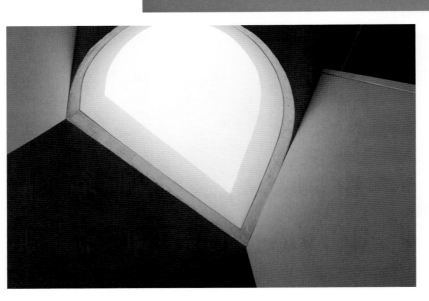

Photos: (top) Jack Pierson – Vault House, South Side Roof 2, 2013; (bottom) James Welling

Johnston Marklee has established itself as an architectural firm engaged with contemporary art practices, drawing on artists, graphic designers, writers, and photographers to broaden the breadth of its research. Such influences inform not only the design process but, more critically, readings of the finished projects. Outsiders' points of view on the architecture often reveal latent elements so powerful that they shift the architects' own understanding of the work. In Johnston Marklee's projects of artist spaces, this process of feedback between artist and architect often interrogates the architectural form beyond its original dimension.

This spirit of collaboration has yielded a series of images produced by artists, inspired by or depicting Johnston Marklee's built projects, creating a dialogue between the artists' personal view and the firm's work. The portfolio includes Jack Pierson on Vault House, James Welling on Porch House, Livia Corona on Sale House, Luisa Lambri on Hill House, Marianne Mueller on various projects, and Veronika Kellndorfer on Hill House.

Historical references are another element that inform Johnston Marklee's designs. In the early phases of a project, collage offers a way of drawing freely and quickly on diverse historical precedents, selecting key elements from existing architecture to establish a lineage with which the project will engage.

*House Is a House Is a House Is a House Is a House* juxtaposes artist photographs—external perspectives on Johnston Marklee's work—with the firm's own reading of each project in the form of collages.

*Project Team*
Sharon Johnston, Mark Lee, Mary Casper, Letizia Garzoli, Grete Grubelich, Sidian Tu

*Artists*
Jack Pierson, James Welling, Livia Corona, Luisa Lambri, Marianne Mueller, Veronika Kellndorfer

44

# JUNYA.ISHIGAMI+ASSOCIATES
## *Tokyo, Japan*
# Kanagawa Institute of Technology

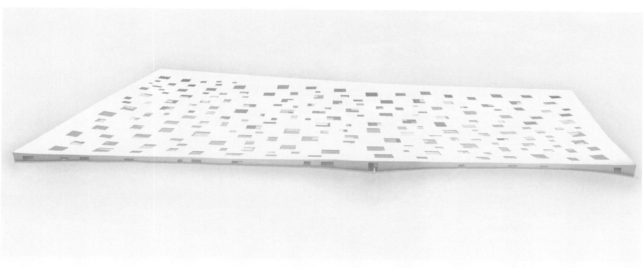

Images: Yasushi Ichikawa

The Kanagawa Institute of Technology workshop is located in the suburbs of Tokyo, on a 21,500 sq. ft. (2,000 m²) site. Various programs are situated within a single, flexible room. Instead of partitioning the building in conventional ways, the project uses points in order to suggest specific spaces while keeping their boundaries ambiguous; the purpose is to experiment with functional flexibility through the notion of abstraction. The points on the plan are, in fact, 305 thin rectangular columns, each with a different size and proportion, which bear all the vertical and horizontal forces (there are no earthquake-resistant walls). The columns would seem to have no rule for their placement, unless examined carefully. People in the building are able to constantly experience the whole expanse of the interior, while simultaneously sensing fluctuations in the shape and size. Strolling around, space seems to be transforming in a continuous flux, like a kaleidoscope.

Adjacent to the KAIT workshop, a semi-covered multipurpose plaza is currently being planned. It is a one-story building measuring approximately 330 × 200 ft. (100 × 60 m). In contrast to the expansive floor plan, the ceiling is 7.5 ft. (2.3 m) high, and is completely devoid of columns. Despite its sheer extent, the structure of the roof is made of a single 0.5 in. (12 mm) thick steel sheet, supported exclusively by the four exterior walls. Ishigami defines this building as a "super delicate mega-structure." By means of its low height, the ceiling maintains a human scale (similar to that of standard Japanese houses) that counteracts the vast horizontal space. The roof is slightly curved in a catenary shape, and the floor traces the same curvature, creating the illusion of the two surfaces meeting each other at a distance. A series of skylights perforate the steel roof, but no glass is installed in these openings. Light, wind, and rain seep through into the space beneath.

*Project Team*
Junya Ishigami and associates

*Acknowledgements*
Konishi Structural Engineers, MEP Environmental Engineering

# KÉRÉ ARCHITECTURE
## *Berlin, Germany*
## Place for Gathering

*Place for Gathering* broaches two themes that are crucial to the work of Francis Kéré: maximizing local resources and facilitating the exchange of ideas and knowledge. As a native of Burkina Faso, Kéré grew up in the rural village of Gando. Located just at the edge of the Sahel, it is a place with challenging climatic conditions and limited resources. Many villages here are remote, and community members depend on one another for the survival and prosperity of the group as a whole. The community helps to rear and educate children, build and maintain housing, and cultivate crops that help to sustain the village. In this sense, the village community can be seen as a large extended family. From an architectural standpoint, it is essential to designate spaces where people can come together and communicate. Whether for celebrating special events, having discussions about important decisions, or simply coming together to gossip and share stories, these common spaces are vital for the everyday functioning of the village.

Kéré Architecture proposes a space for visitors to reflect upon and discuss these ideas. Built simply, with locally sourced wood, the *Place for Gathering* is a seating terrain where visitors can connect in a basic and informal way. The intervention makes space for differing cultural narratives, traditions, and aspirations to be celebrated and shared.

*Project Team*
Diébédo Francis Kéré, Adriana Arteaga, Dominique Mayer, Diego Sologuren Martin, Ines Bergdolt, Yara Pavel, Jaime Herraiz Martínez, Daniel Heuermann

*Acknowledgements*
Blake Villwock

46

# KUEHN MALVEZZI + ARMIN LINKE + MARKO LULIĆ
## *Berlin, Germany*
## Models of the House of One

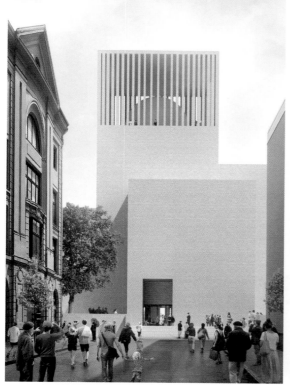

The center of Berlin will be the site for the House of One, a house of prayer and learning for Jews, Christians, and Muslims alike, as well as the secular urban community. Kuehn Malvezzi designed a synagogue, a church, and a mosque to be built under one and the same roof. The House of One's potential results from the simultaneity of intimacy and foreignness, from similarities and differences between the three Abrahamic religions.

*Models of the House of One* exposes us to the project's potential through a concrete spatial experience, where three models come together in one installation. The *Model of Spaces* is a sculpture, in which the interior spaces of the House of One are displayed as a negative volume at a 1:8 scale. In the *Model of Gestures*, Armin Linke's photographs follow the liturgical actions of Jews, Christians, and Muslims in their respective sacred spaces. The *Model of Relations* explores possible modes of interrelation within a collective space, in the form of a performance choreographed by Marko Lulić.

The architecture of the House of One is monumental and devoid of symbolism, and presents itself to the city as a single entity. The spatial experience of the interior, however, contrasts with this perception; inside, the three religions assert their autonomy and differences. The synagogue, church, and mosque are each independently sculpted into the building mass, their form based on the different liturgies.

The three sacred spaces are grouped around a central square shaped as a high-domed hall, making this fourth room at once a junction and the main space. The simultaneity of similarities and differences culminates here; the programmatic vagueness of the central square leads it to oscillate between these poles. The space operates both as interstitial void and as a space of encounter that expands the urban realm of Berlin into the building.

In a spatial sense, the House of One enables the three monotheistic religions — related to one another but also estranged — to engage with one another and with the secular urban community.

### Project Team
Simona Malvezzi, Johannes Kuehn, Wilfried Kuehn, Armin Linke, Marko Lulić, Bérénice Corret, Christian Felgendreher, Samuel Korn, Anna Naumann, Yu Ninagawa, Felix Rohde, Mira Schröder, Carolin Würthner

# LATERAL OFFICE
## *Toronto, Canada*
## Making Camp

From Henry David Thoreau's cabin in the woods to nineteenth-century estates and twentieth-century cottages, offering urbanites respite from the city, the notion of retreat and of the restorative role of immersive landscape experiences has been central to North American culture. Camping in North America did not develop on a large scale until after World War II, when leisure time, car use and the possibility of camping with motorized vehicles greatly expanded. This growth was served by both public and commercial campsites, which offered a range of camping experiences. Private campgrounds catered to recreational vehicles, or RVs, by offering paved parking areas in picturesque locations. Public camp grounds, often in national and provincial parks, offered both remote campsites and more accessible "car camping." The layout of car camping sites embraced a suburban plan, complete with cul-de-sac roads, and different lots visually sheltered by trees but within viewing and hearing distance of each other—the car pulling up to each lot as the first act of setting up camp.

Both private campgrounds and government-run parks offer a range of services, from electrical hookups, water, showers and bathrooms to Wi-Fi access and small-scale retail. There have equally been many technical advances in camping gear, from tents to mattresses, from lounge furniture to dish sets, from cooking devices to lighting devices, striving toward lighter weight and enhanced performance. These enhancements make it easier for the average camper to access increasingly remote or difficult sites, while shifting the camping experience ever closer to a familiar, comfortable domestic experience.

The enduring appeal of camping over the past century seems to be a return to the proverbial "primitive hut"—the desire for immersive experiences while reducing the envelopes and infrastructures that traditionally separate us from our environment. Yet, we are increasingly removed from this experience, embracing a suburban relationship to wilderness. Is there a possibility for other forms of collectivity in isolation?

*Making Camp* looks at possible evolutions for twenty-first-century camping. It questions the sites we might have access to, the experiences that are enabled, and the environments created by these camping infrastructures. A series of five prototypes explores a range of typologies, landscapes, and degrees of user customization: towers enabling occupation of the forest's tree canopy, platforms hovering above wetlands, floating dock islands to allow a retreat from land itself, cliffside occupations, and netted structures that redefine ground. Each solution, while offering new collective camping experiences, doubles as a public platform for experiencing the landscape in new ways.

*Project Team*
Lola Sheppard (partner), Mason White (partner),
Alexander Bodkin (project lead), Kinan Hewitt,
Safoura Zahedi, Laurence Holland, Cherry Fung,
Kate Holbrook-Smith, Daniela Leon, Karan Manchanda

# LCLA OFFICE
## *Medellín, Colombia / Cambridge, US*
## Islands, Atolls, and Other Derivative Territories

*Islands, Atolls, and Other Derivative Territories* is a textile illustration that shows the tension between two-dimensional architectural methods of representation and the depiction of fluid landscapes. It tests the capacity of drawing to represent large-scale landscape events and tropical plant material. The 23 × 16 ft. (7 × 5 m) silk fabric was developed by LCLA's Luis Callejas in collaboration with architect and fashion designer Charlotte Hansson. Four photographs taken by Callejas, during his travels between arctic and tropical geographies point to the original landscapes that were the basis for the scenes depicted in the silk piece.

*Project Team*
Luis Callejas, Charlotte Hansson

*Acknowledgements*
Giancarlo Mazzanti; Paisajes Emergentes

# LIST
## *Paris, France*
## Sports Park Genk

The initial impetus of LIST's project was a 164 ft. (50 m) wide space separating a swimming pool that was built in the early 1970s and a new sports arena in the Belgian city of Genk. The newly created gap, in the middle of a pleasant, green park, seemed an ideal place for a public square. In order to do more than simply connect the existing buildings, the space was split in three: a Forest Strip, an Esplanade and a Park Connector —all three being equally important and forming one single public sequence.

The Forest Strip is a very long and thin pedestrian and bike lane, which runs through the forest following the topography. The lightweight concrete infrastructure is largely covered by tree canopy and connects the sports fields to one another. Benches and small fountains can be found on its north side, while bike parking places are scattered on its south side. At sunset, the strip is illuminated with fairy lights suspended from the trees.

The two existing buildings, though imposing in their architecture, have little to offer in terms of urban life. The space between them was thus defined as an Esplanade—a term that refers to a flat square originally placed at the edge of the city. The Esplanade functions as a third entity relating more to the open landscape of the Stiemerbeek Valley than to the two buildings. It is designed as a sand platform inscribed inside a 115 × 197 ft. (35 × 60 m) natural-stone edge. The platform cantilevers from the slope, creating a balcony overlooking the valley.

The parking lot currently facing the two buildings induces a suburban relationship between visitors and the sports park—as if going to IKEA. By reorienting it and optimizing its design, LIST made it possible to interrupt the one-dimensional relationship, creating a Park Connector from which all the different functions can be easily reached.

*Project Team*
Ido Avissar, Thaïs de Roquemaurel, Emily Game, Léonor Chabason, Quentin Madiot, Laetitia Chavanne

*Acknowledgements*
LOLA Landscape Architects, ANTEA Engineering Group

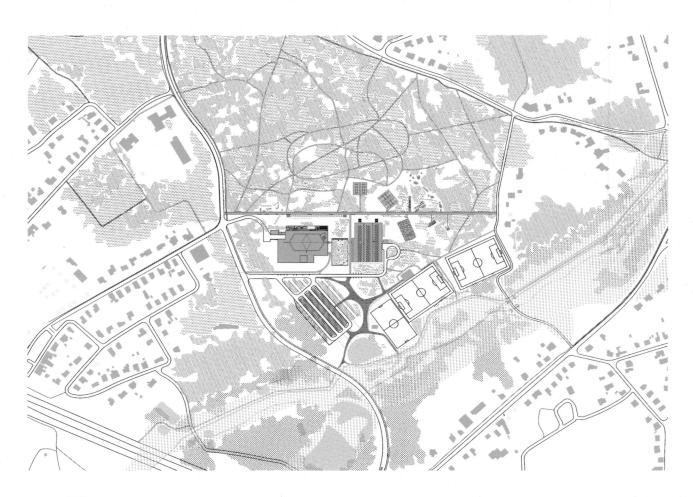

# MAIO
## *Barcelona, Spain*
## Floating: The Presence of the Present

*Floating* is a spatial activator for public discussion. It is a manifesto installation that aims to provide a response to the question of the state of the art of architecture by means of its very design: it is siteless, systemic, unfinished, ready-made.

*Floating* takes the commons as a starting point. It amplifies other architectures, provokes things into happening, and allows critical dialogues about the current state of the field to open up.

Now more than ever, space has lost any unidirectional definition and has thus become a field of possible actions where anything can happen at the same time. As architecture's outlines have become dimmer, the quest for a characterization of a state of the art leads us to the conclusion that architecture is made of infinite and ever-changing attitudes materializing in different forms.

Today, the comprehensiveness and immediacy of networks have produced an alteration in the relationship between space and function by making evident that boundaries are changing and the very nature of architecture is shifting. Heterotopic spaces—which, as defined in the 1960s, blurred existing hierarchies—have become more complex, and it seems necessary to define an architectural answer to the needs of the heterotopic society inhabiting them.

*Floating* is a ready-made architecture that can be continuously reconfigured. Each *Floating* unit is an inflatable structure, forming part of a wider system that allows to shape different spaces as required. Thanks to its lightness, each unit can be easily moved depending on the site and audience. The structure is in a permanently unfinished state. It can be moved around a building, showing up in different places and with different configurations. Architecture is not about what it is, it is about what it can be.

*Project Team*
Maria Charneco, Alfredo Lérida, Guillermo López, Anna Puigjaner, Miguel Bernat

# MAKEKA DESIGN LAB
## *Cape Town, South Africa*
## Transcape: New Horizons

Photos: (top) Peter K Photography; (bottom) Dave Southwood

The single largest task that humanity will face in the twenty-first century is the role and performance of cities, their inhabitants, and the vast terrains that sustain them.

African and Asian cities will bear the brunt of a population explosion, the result of which will cause a significant portion of humanity to occupy self-managed shanty towns beyond the reach of traditional urban governance.

The history of the African continent is a troubled one. Its fragmented urbanism is a testament to the failure of human imagination to anticipate how its cities would grow over time, which is compounded by residual colonial and often race-based spatial planning. Property markets continue to unfold on this existing base, reproducing—despite legislated equity and a growing culture of human rights—the conditions of spatialized inequality.

Modernity as a construct has had vast ongoing social and spatial implications for humanity, and its various regional distortions have produced Cities with a precarious infrastructural legacy worldwide. Urban centers of the Global South, thriving with spatial and economic contradictions, embody a radical rupture from the current normative understanding of what a city should be.

In the case of South Africa the legacy of apartheid, where urban planning strategies distorted infrastructure into a social engineering device, continues to affect architectural production. In a milieu of increasing urban disharmony, rapid demographic change, nascent democracies, and a diminishing agency of the architect, public infrastructures are detached from public interest, raising debates about the production of civic architecture. In this context, architecture has yet to produce an aesthetic regime detached from the past.

Through the lens of Cape Town and its visceral contradictions, *Transcape: New Horizons* reveals cross-continental commonalities, and the importance of anticipatory architecture in the context of emerging and precarious cultural dialogues.

*Project Team*
Mokena Makeka, Etienne du Plooy, Yolandi Viljoen, Richard Mandy, in collaboration with Koketso Kujane (Riot Republic)

# MARK WASIUTA, MARCOS SANCHEZ, ADAM BANDLER + GSAPP EXHIBITIONS
## *New York City / Los Angeles, US*
# Environmental Communications: Contact High

*Environmental Communications: Contact High* is the first major public display of the prolific West Coast architecture and media collective Environmental Communications. Formed by a group of young architects, photographers, and psychologists in the late 1960s, Environmental Communications argued that in an era of accelerating image proliferation, university slide libraries were the emerging centers of institutional and pedagogical power. The group's core members, David Greenberg, Bernard Perloff, Ted Tokio Tanaka, and Roger Webster, speculated that by infiltrating slide libraries with their "environmental photography," they could alter the visual cortex of architecture schools, subvert conventional pedagogy, and spark a revolution in student consciousness.

Environmental photography entailed a process of sensitizing oneself to the spatial, mediatic, and social conditions that the group documented in Tokyo, the American Southwest, and, most often, Los Angeles, their primary object of analysis. Through this visual practice, Environmental Communications pursued their goal of developing, and becoming, "systems of perception." They eventually shot hundreds of thousands of 35 mm slides, forming a vast visual taxonomy of Southern California's urban and social geography. Compiled into thematic sets with titles such as "Human Territoriality in the City," "Urban Crowd Behavior," and "Pedestrian Space," the slides were packaged and sold via the Environmental Communications catalogue to museums, cultural institutions, and to an international network of architecture schools.

At their studio in Venice, the hub of Southern California's counterculture, the group organized happenings and video festivals, while reflecting on the state of architectural education and formulating a mediatized counter-pedagogy. Through

their slide catalogues they became both interpreters and purveyors of new architectural and environmental trends. Their slide series mapped the domes, inflatables, communes, and media experiments of the late 1960s and 1970s, compiling an almanac of the era's alternative architectural practices. Booklets printed to accompany the sets offered instructive descriptions of each slide and brief essays that served as condensed primers on architecture's environmental thought.

*Contact High* surveys Environmental Communications' experimental practices from process images, videotaped road trips, blimp tours, and group therapy sessions to the increasingly polished multimedia packets distributed through their catalogues. The project was first produced by GSAPP Exhibitions for the Arthur Ross Architecture Gallery at Columbia University's Graduate School of Architecture, Planning and Preservation.

*Project Team*
Mark Wasiuta, Marcos Sanchez, Adam Bandler (project curators and designers); Florencia Alvarez Pacheco (curatorial assistant); Alissa Anderson, Virginia Black, Rebecca Book, Maite Borjabad, Maryam Fotouhi, Liyana Hasnan, Andrew Hite, Emily Mohr, Megan Murdock, Sareeta Patel, Rayna Razmilic, Brittany Roy, Tania Tovar Torres (GSAPP assistants)

*Acknowledgements*
All images and documents courtesy of Environmental Communications (David Greenberg, Bernard Perloff, Ted Tokio Tanaka, Roger Webster)

# MASS STUDIES + HYUN-SUK SEO
## *Seoul, Korea*
## Zoom Out / Zone Out

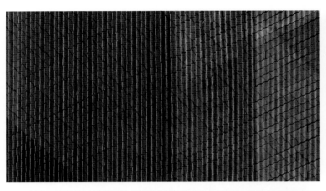

*Zoom Out / Zone Out* is a moving composition of multiple photographic narratives based on the work of Mass Studies. Using the work of thirteen photographers to portray thirty-nine built projects, it is the inevitable confrontation between architectural construction and an era of digital photographic production.

The visuals that flicker through the film are extracted from thousands of sequences of construction documents and other archival materials, which have been reordered and collapsed into more than 400 photographs. *Zoom Out / Zone Out* is an inventory of viewing typologies or an attempt to process the contemporary overload of spatial information into a comprehensive experience.

Each building's specific, individual moments are revisited by its architect, Minsuk Cho, and artist Hyun-Suk Seo, and rearranged into an *an-archive*. The montage fuses multiple projects into one heterogeneous flux of spaces, gradually shifting the scale of vision—zooming out and zoning out—from the extreme intimacy of material textures all the way to aerial perspectives.

This dynamic performance is a fragmentary visual and auditory combination of architectural structures and cinematic imaginations, based on the aesthetics of film noir. It is an anarchic subversion of the typical linear representation of architectural archives.

*Project Team*
Minsuk Cho, Hyun-Suk Seo, Sunny Park, Betty Kim, Hyunsoo Ha, Cheon-Kang Park

*Photographers*
Yong-Kwan Kim, Kyungsub Shin, Iwan Baan, Kiyoshi Ota, Jan Edler, Sungpil Won, Jason Walp, Jungsik Moon, Gaia Cambiaggi, Kyenyong Kwak, Gyeong-Whoi Ahn, Wansoo Park, Eric Xu

# MOON HOON
## *Seoul, Korea*
## Doodle Constructivism

Doodling is central to Moon Hoon's conception of architecture; he has been drawing compulsively for more than forty years. The sketches, double A4 pages in moleskin notebooks that the Korean architect fills in his spare time and during eight-hour meditative sessions on weekends, have an intimate relationship with his architecture, expressing structures that can't be built, ideas that augment or derive from what he has already designed, or concepts that are expressed in architectural form.

Moon Hoon grew up in a coal-mining town in Sangdong, Korea, and memories of that environment—reminiscent of Russian constructivist drawings or the movie *Total Recall* —feed into his doodles, as do various religious, philosophical, and literary ideas. The methods of other architects famous for using drawing as an expressive medium, such as Lebbeus Woods, are explicitly referenced in his work. Eroticism, seduction, and tantric Buddhism are also evoked. More recently, Hoon's drawing practice has become akin to journaling, dealing with such mundane topics as his lunch or translating his thoughts of that day into architectural form.

Several of his sketches are now part of the collection of the Tchoban Foundation in Berlin, and an anthology of drawings has been published under the title *Doodle My Way to the Moon*. *Doodle Constructivism* is a sampling of his sketchbooks, showing sketches connected to recent projects, such as Rock It Suda and Wind House, as well as more speculative drawings.

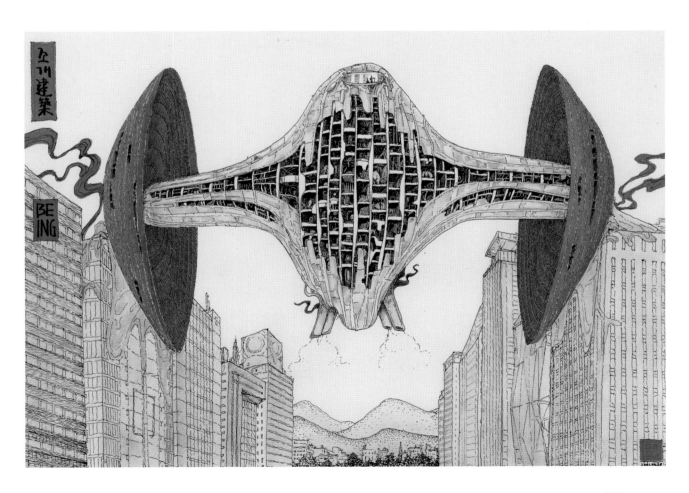

# MOS ARCHITECTS
## *New York City, US*
# House No. 11 (Corridor House)

At some point, before the existence of Twitter, the corridor killed a certain type of architecture. Courtyards collapsed into light wells; diagrams became buildings. It was all about transit, all the time. Architecture focused on the circulation of things, people, air, light, goods, etc. Space became a lubricant. It was almost spiritual. Architecture embraced the new efficiency of the short circuit, a faster way of getting from one place to another. As space was replaced with movement, stuff was jettisoned, and the leftovers piled up. Nowadays, corridors are a necessary afterthought, an indifferent chasm joining this to that in houses everywhere.

*House No. 11* occupies that circuitry. It is one variation among many: an assembly of parts that are both technical and archetypal. It vaguely resembles the strange figures of suburban corridors along with the openness of a Miesian courtyard house. Each module approximates the dimensions of a standard corridor and of a sheet of plywood measuring 5 × 10 ft. (1.5 × 3 m).

Yet, many such corridor spaces are large enough to be inhabited and to contain a small room (bed, desk, chair). Each module is positioned orthogonally to its neighbor. The overall configuration is loosely organized around a collection of exterior spaces but is disconnected from the ground. It's repetitive. It's made of parts. It's casual. It's almost familiar. It's nothing in particular. It fits on a truck.

*Project Team*
Michael Meredith, Hilary Sample, John Yurchyk, Cyrus Dochow, Michael Abel, Mark Acciari, Ryan Barney, Phi Phan

*Acknowledgements*
Remont Construction, Cabinets by Stanley, Silman Engineers, Juan Garcia Mosqueda

# NEW-TERRITORIES / M4
## *Bangkok, Thailand*
## #mythomaniaS

... Psychotic machines, psychotic apparatuses and fragments ... Bodies in verse, bodies-becoming ... are meeting in the stories of their symptoms ... plausible. The "forbidden" is reintroduced as a possible, and what was rejected or considered as an improper ingredient within our computer graphic idealization of the world is coming back like ... Lines of Subjectivities vs. Functionalism, Bodies vs. Body, Substances vs. Design, Scenario vs. Concept ... Pataphysics vs. pseudo-scientific Positivism ... Vanitas vs. Naivism ... Environments and paranoia as symptoms of an inner condition, in a constant exchange between narrative and emergence, in a stuttering process: a storytelling manifested in the creation of a fiction which uses a fragment as a by-product and where a material structure with its physical characteristics takes shape and instructs the story (schizoid protocols within miscibility and autonomy ... ), through Mythomania of each situation, of each character ... transforming environments with their para-psyches, confusing ... confronted to different biotopes and feedback ... in a permanent challenge to articulate the contingencies of logic between the instruments-tooling ... as computation, as robotic, as "de-expertise" ... with ... at the opposite ... the discovering of the potential of a masochism adaptation, for a kind of situationist claim or debt ... in a strategy-tragedy of correlations ... of co-dependencies ... for prototyping discourses and substances, material and immaterial ... and pornography.

*Project Team*
François Roche, Camille Lacadee

*Partners*
Stephan Henrich, Ezio Blasetti, Gwyl Jahn, Pierre Huyghe, Carsten Holler, Danielle Willems, Devin Jernigan, Galo Moncayo Asan, Peter Griebel, Gabrielle Cram, Giorgio Pace

*Collaborators*
Vongsawat Wongkijjalerd, Daniela Mitterberger, Tiziano Derme, Myrtille Fakhreddine, Agatha Partyka, Katrin Hochschuh, Hadin Charbel, Amaury Thomas, Lydia Kalipoliti, Marc Ihle

*Acknowledgements*
CNC DICREAM Paris; RMIT; University of Pennsylvania; Innsbruck Hochbau; Columbia GSAPP; INDA Chulalongkorn; Donau Festival; Singapore Biennale; Graham Foundation; Nouveau Musée National de Monaco

*Full credits are available at new-territories.com/props.htm*

# NIKOLAUS HIRSCH / MICHEL MÜLLER
## *Frankfurt, Germany*
## Exquisite Corpse: A Studio Residency for The Land

*With David Adjaye, Markus Binder, Bollinger + Grohmann, Aroon Puritat + Sumeth Klahan + Chayanon Hansapinyo, Tobias Rehberger, Tomás Saraceno, Superflex*

The Land, initiated by Rirkrit Tiravanija and Kamin Lertchaiprasert, is a self-sustaining environment and artistic community located near Chiang Mai, Thailand. It is intended to be an open space free of ownership, an environment conducive to discussions and experimentation. The Land is open to the day-to-day activities of local life—the cultivation of rice, for instance—and to the neighboring community. As a "social field," artistic practices are discussed and tested there, juxtaposing contemporary materials with ancient practices.

The latest project at The Land, conceived by architects Nikolaus Hirsch and Michel Müller, is a structure that comprises studios, a workshop space, and shelter. The act of "building" is the result of a collaborative process involving a group of leading architects, engineers, and artists to reflect on the larger political, socioeconomic, and cultural context that is understood as a "site." The building will evolve as a collective assemblage according to the sequential logic of its spaces. In each step, one element will be added, each designed by a different author: foundation, structure, façade, energy, services, and studios.

In architecture, it is broadly assumed that the spatial-physical entity of a building must imply a coherent language conceived by a single author—usually, the architect. The studio-residency project for The Land takes the opposite approach: the loss of control, usually bemoaned by designers, is a potential for new architecture. The aim is to investigate new practices of building that use the logic and language of a collaborative workshop to question notions of coherence and homogeneity.

The 72 × 72 ft. (22 × 22 m) building is partitioned into autonomous yet related components. The sequential construction process usually unseen is exposed like a surrealist "exquisite corpse," a collective work that begins with a single contribution and continues to grow step by step. Never finished, it knows no endgame.

*Acknowledgements*
Emmi Wegener, Matthias Görlich, Kamin Lertchaiprasert, Rirkrit Tiravanija

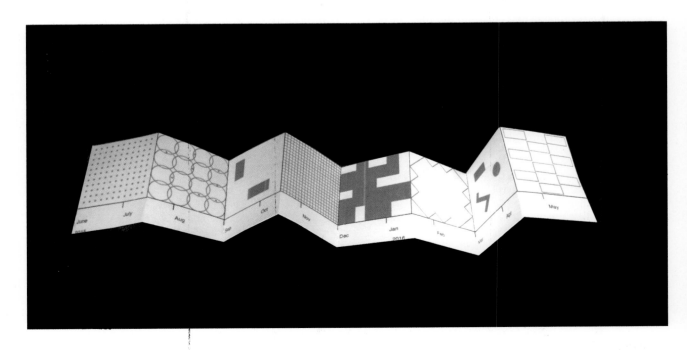

# NOERO ARCHITECTS
## *Cape Town, South Africa*
## 180 Square Meters

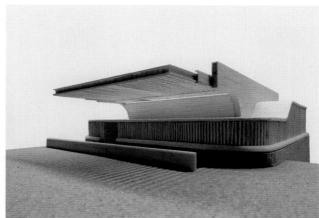

One of the most complex issues facing architects in a country like South Africa is working in a context of high levels of inequality and extreme contrasts between the ways in which the rich and the poor live in and occupy cities. In most cases, South African architects choose to work among the rich for sensible commercial reasons. A much smaller number of architects work among the poor and the dispossessed, usually collaborating with NGOs or state agencies.

Practicing for more than thirty years, Jo Noero has chosen to work simultaneously in both sectors, allowing one to subsidize the other. This kind of practice involves considerable negotiations between one's political sensibilities and one's need to survive.

Noero does not believe that architecture, by itself, is able to create revolutionary change in society—at best, it can assist in creating the necessary conditions for change. This position creates a clear distinction between one's responsibilities as an architect and those associated with active citizenship. To collapse the distinction between these two sets of actions would both diminish the architectural potential of the work and weaken any revolutionary potential that might exist.

Noero felt the need to establish an ethical sensibility with regard to his work, so that he wouldn't lose sight of what he considers to be important in architecture. This sensibility includes not designing private houses larger than 1,950 sq. ft. (180 m²), keeping in mind South Africa's long-standing housing shortage. He also interviews all potential clients to ensure that their values and goals are in line with his own.

*180 Square Meters* juxtaposes two houses Noero designed —one of about 1,880 sq. ft. (175 m²) for a wealthy family; the other a state-subsidized house of about 470 sq. ft. (44 m²) for a low-income family. The first house occupies a beautiful site adjacent to the sea on the Cape Peninsula coast. The second house is part of a larger public project that Noero Architects is building in New Brighton, Port Elizabeth. Both buildings serve important, albeit different, social needs and consequently carry a similar set of ethical considerations.

While the first structure is for a family who simply wanted a well-designed space, the family in New Brighton will receive their housing from the state, as part of the process of redistributing wealth in South Africa. Both homes have been designed with the same amount of care and attention.

*Project Team*
Jo Noero, Evandro Schwalbach, Korine Stegman,
Michael Hobbs

*Acknowledgements*
Jimmy Tutu (ANC councilor for Red Location); Rory Riordan
(independent development consultant)

# NORMAN KELLEY
## *Chicago / New York City, US*
## Chicago: How Do You See?

When you look at Chicago outside the window, how do you see?

Norman Kelley clads the sixty-five windows on the Michigan Avenue façade of the Chicago Cultural Center with sixty-five drawings of other Chicago windows. Each glass panel is lined with white-cut vinyl, which mediates the gaze into the building and out onto the city.

The graphic motif is visible from Michigan Avenue's east sidewalk and presents an oversized survey of historical window mullions and dressings, ranging from Arts & Crafts to Chicago School patterns to vernacular window treatments (like venetian blinds and pleated curtains).

By sourcing new and old ways Chicagoans use to look at the urban landscape, Norman Kelley presents a plurality of points of view as a collective vision of the city.

*Project Team*
Thomas Kelley, Carrie Norman, Spencer McNeil

# OFFICE KERSTEN GEERS DAVID VAN SEVEREN + BAS PRINCEN
## *Brussels, Belgium / Rotterdam, The Netherlands*
## Model for a Pavilion (Thinkbelt)

Photos: Bas Princen with OFFICE KGDVS, "The Wall Pavilion"

Before and after Gottfried Semper's thesis on architecture and textiles, various incarnations of the tent-like space have appeared in radically different architectural environments. In some ways, both Friedrich Schinkel's tent room and Hannes Meyer's Co-op interior are incarnations of the same, a mise-en-scène of an idea of architecture that is both light and ephemeral, demonstrating its raw organizing power while in denial about its most evident tectonics. The textile here is capable of showing a spatial architecture of "almost nothing." Of course, neither Semper's treatise nor Schinkel and Meyer's pavilions are anomalies, and they were not intended as such. They are able to communicate the unresolvable conflict between the intentions that create architecture as space —a result of a somewhat evolving set of principles—and the literal desire to make a pure, simple, and coherent structure.

Cedric Price's Potteries Thinkbelt is both emblematic and exemplary of his work. Its proposal to transform a rail track into a linear machine for learning makes it an epitome of the technical modernist dream—functional and direct, a literal architecture. At the same time its inherent ephemerality —both in design and representation—represents the modernist project consciously gone berserk. The *Thinkbelt* is fully aware of its limitations and is free from any formal desire: a machine to accommodate. The fact that it was not realized perhaps adds to its status. It remains a phantom of modernism, a radical critique from within.

Where the *Thinkbelt* was planned, there is a fragment of beautiful, unmaintained wilderness today, a piece of unkempt England after modernism. Bas Princen took a series of photographs of the Madeley Transfer Area, the background of the most iconic drawing of the project, thus picturing the fact that the Thinkbelt was never realized.

The intervention by OFFICE KGDVS is another incarnation of an ongoing investigation into the limits of both architectural materialization and photographic illusion. With Princen, they attempt to make a model of a space, showing some of the photographs of the Thinkbelt series printed on "life scale." The result is a life-sized model that makes the spatial illusion tangible. A sequence of the photographs makes a continuous curtain, a perimeter simplifying the existing borders of the room. It hovers above eye height, thus creating a diorama of sorts: a view of the site of the Potteries Thinkbelt from within, a panorama room. Even though the curtain itself is the actual intervention, it turns the walls of the existing room into the space from which we look at the Madeley Transfer Area. In some way, the effect is that of a glass house, a space that depends on pure illusion, an architecture capable of doing more with nothing at all.

*Project Team*
Kersten Geers, David Van Severen, Bas Princen, Nenad Duric

*Acknowledgements*
Stefano Graziani

# ONISHIMAKI + HYAKUDAYUKI ARCHITECTS
## *Tokyo, Japan*
## Children's Town

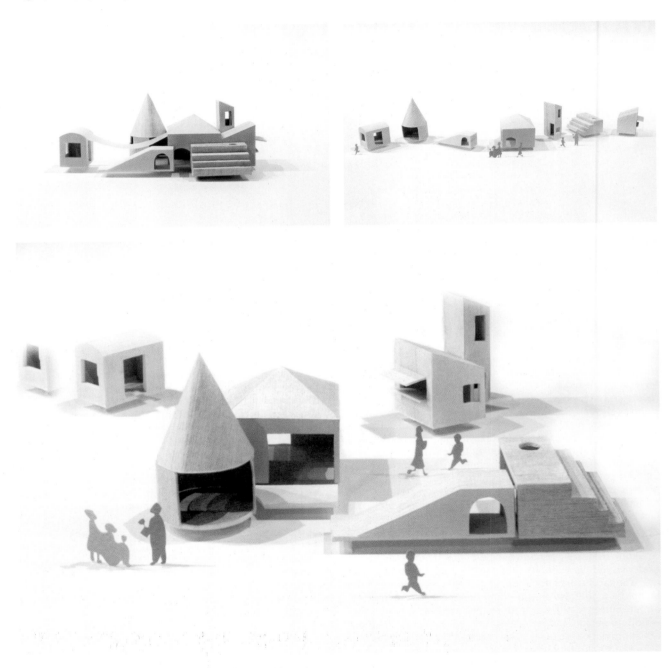

***Children's Town*** is a small town for children. It is a gathering of several small houses, all of which are on wheels, so they can be moved. Children can parade with the houses or change their layout to make a new town in which to play.

*Project Team*
Maki Onishi, Yuki Hyakuda, Shiho Eika, Meiri Shinohara, Takeshi Yamazaki, Makoto Furusawa

# OPEN ARCHITECTURE +
# SPIRIT OF SPACE
## *Beijing, China / Chicago, US*
## An OPEN Manifesto

Nearly a hundred years after the film *L'architecture d'aujourd'hui*, which was a collaboration between filmmaker Pierre Chenal and Le Corbusier, Beijing-based OPEN Architecture and Spirit of Space from Chicago join forces to use film as a medium to make a visual manifesto on contemporary architecture in China today. Cinematic representation captures the spirit of OPEN's works, which are often designed from the inside out with a focus on the behavior of people and their interaction with buildings.

The history of urbanism in China is being quickly rewritten. The future of the Chinese people is being built in haste, often without careful planning or conscientious execution. Throughout the history of Chinese cities, public spaces have been almost nonexistent. With China's race to modernity in an age of globalization, the historical urban structure is no longer functional; but new structures are yet to be established. We urgently need cities that are open and adaptable to the modernizing Chinese society. We see a great need for public spaces of all forms and scales, open and free, serving society at large.

In the films, shot by Spirit of Space, the visual narrative is built around three key topics, as embodied by four of OPEN Architecture's built projects: China and its urban dynamics, the process of architectural creation, and poetry through behavior.

*Project Team*
Li Hu, Huang Wenjing, Chen Cheng, Joshua Parker (OPEN Architecture); Adam Goss, Red Mike, Ryan Clark (Spirit of Space)

Images: Spirit of Space

# OTHEROTHERS
## *Sydney, Australia*
## Offset House

Hidden within every suburban house is a great work of architecture. Look beneath shallow eaves and brick veneer, behind ornate porticos, skirting boards, cornices, and drywall, and you'll find modernism's most successful and longest-running project. Invented and industrialized in nineteenth-century Chicago, balloon-frame timber construction made individual housing simple, fast, and widely accessible. Basic variants of this system remain in use around the world. Seen silhouetted against the sky, before cladding is applied and fences erected, the naked timber frame is a thing of elemental beauty, a lacework diagram of infinite potential. Simply put, the frame is architecture.

While Australian architecture is associated with bespoke pavilions in idyllic wilderness settings, mass-produced suburban housing is the norm. Australians have the largest average home sizes and living space of any nation. Twenty-four million people occupy an area larger than the continental US, which has thirteen times the population. Australia is both one of the world's most urbanized nations and among the least dense. The country's interior is sparsely populated, and fewer than 10 percent of Australians live in close proximity to a city center—most inhabit the suburban in-between.

Suburbia is not just home for most Australians: it is the primary domain of social exchange, cultural relations, and political discourse. In his influential 1960 book *Australian Ugliness*, Robin Boyd equated the brick-veneer suburban house with the nation's racist White Australia policy. More recently, Pritzker Prize–winning architect Glenn Murcutt claimed that suburban houses are "not architecture." But if the language of the McMansion is merely a veneer, shouldn't Australian architects see right through it?

*Offset House* aims to reveal the beauty and utility of the frame, peeling away layers of anachronistic construction, poor planning, and illogical furnishings. By reclaiming the frame for architecture, we hope to reframe our relationship to the suburbs. The project proposes the adaptive reuse of houses in Sydney's Kellyville. Typical of suburban Australia, these cheaply built dwellings fill almost all of their plots. The architectural strategy involves literally "offsetting" each house's structure. A new layer of structure is nested within the volume of the original; the line of external cladding removed and transferred to the inner frame.

The zone between the two frames becomes a verandah, providing shading, privacy, ventilation, and spatial flexibility. Reducing enclosed dwelling space enables downsizing without relocation, with tangible energy and resource savings. Surrounded by a permeable outer skin, the house no longer requires fences. Vestigial space between houses is consolidated into a shared commons, providing space for gardening, recreation, and play, and reorienting the block away from the road. The cyclical renewal of suburban houses promises to reinvigorate moribund outer suburbs, allowing for generational and cultural change.

*Project Team*
Grace Mortlock, David Neustein, Jordan Soriot, Christopher Argent

*Acknowledgements*
Australian Consulate-General Chicago

64

# P-A-T-T-E-R-N-S + CASEY REHM
## *Los Angeles, US*
## Oblicuo

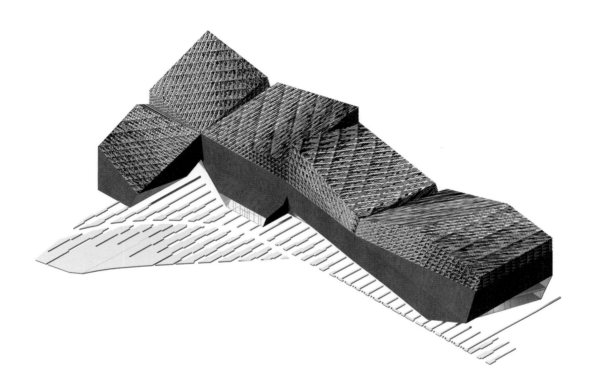

*Oblicuo* challenges fixed aesthetic notions of beauty and legibility in architectural representation, using abstraction and defamiliarization to speculate on the generation of photo-realistic images, especially as it relates to the role and present status of architectural icons.

The P-A-T-T-E-R-N-S proposals for Budapest City Park form the backdrop for a loose network of four discrete architectural objects that engage the contemporary notion of the image as a mute entity.

The original proposal took cues from the medieval style and imposing nature of the existing castles as a contrast to the lush and idyllic landscape of the park, addressing the outlines of cupolas, vaulted domes, high-pitched roofs, and other neoclassical elements in the area that create an idiosyncratic skyline. Through subtle forms and fuzzy textures, the architecture sought to adopt a mysterious urban attitude by abstracting its context.

By revisiting the Budapest project, *Oblicuo* aims to experiment with the limits and possibilities of technologically aided image-making and hyperenhanced realism, to reveal both the hidden inconsistencies and newfound potentials of this medium to define new speculative realities for architecture.

Technically, *Oblicuo* leverages the underlying biases and discrepancies in contemporary methods of computer visualization to generate a novel understanding of both context and field in architecture. By purposefully misappropriating and retooling common algorithms that are used to create coherent representations of urban environments from distributed sources, *Oblicuo* exposes the seams, voids, and flaws concealed by the hidden agencies that continuously manipulate our perception of the world.

In its purposeful dichotomy and vague indeterminacy as both a *plan oblique* and a photo-realistic image, *Oblicuo* contests long-standing antagonisms—between abstraction and realism, simulation and representation, perspective and projection, object and field, drawing and image. The speculative nature of its result exposes the disciplinary potential of these machines in their ability to both perceive and transform our world in ever-finer ways.

*Project Team*
Marcelo Spina, Georgina Huljich, Casey Rehm, Carlos Navarro, Stefan Svedberg, Anthony Stoffella, Eda Yetim, Dylan Krueger, Xingtai Sun, Kellan Cartledge

# PEDRO&JUANA
## *Mexico City, Mexico*
# Randolph

Dear Randolph,

Do you remember when the Chicago Cultural Center used to be the public library? Do you remember Randolph Square on the side of Randolph Street? The newspaper stands inside allowing Chicagoans to read the latest edition of the daily papers? Strange to call it a square, it being indoors. Anyways, Randolph Square used to be the place to go and get the latest news, or just to look at the pictures. Imagine the social encounters, political discussions, and mafia gossip that went on in and around that square.

Then the books moved out of the building and with them went the newsstands, the gossip, and the political discussions. The nature and program of Randolph Square started to change, as did the infrastructure of the aging building. Gas was switched off, and the sconces converted to electrical lighting. When the Tiffany dome started leaking, a state-of-the-art concrete shell was built over it. No more daylight, and electricity did the job. Tiles started popping out of the floor. Vinyl was discussed, but carpet won. Then came fluorescent lighting. Maybe that was before the carpet. My memory is spotty, hence not truthful.

The building was to be torn down, but since it was funded by a 1 percent tax levied on the population of Chicago, the people remembered that it was actually theirs. And Randolph Square transformed into something else.

Today it is called "the living room of the city"—imagine something intimately public! The carpet came off, and the tiles came back. And there the square stands, bare but for the marble-clad walls and columns. Quite modern, but also quite Roman, inside a building of Victorian excess. A bunch of unwieldy tables, some from a French bistro, some

seemingly from the Middle Ages, populates the space. Not too living-room-like, in the end, except for the lunchtime dancing on the first and third Fridays of the month.

The latest rumor: change again! Some architects are going to take out the fluorescent lighting in the ceiling coffers, replacing them with a web of thick string and spheres similar to the gas-lit sconces from back in the day. The system alters its shape through a manual push and pull, transforming light and shadow, promising a sensation of change throughout the day. The Roman marble walls will be dressed in Greek paint to reconnect with the original ceiling.

The space will be unstable, aiming to fulfill an ideal of domesticity in the public domain. There will be rockers to rock on, to grant a degree of porch-sitting autonomy, sofas to lie on, tables to stand at. Slight typological transgressions that hint at something else. They will all add up to create a conversation between the body and the object, or maybe just between the furniture and the Chicagoans who use it.

Yours truly,

Pedro&Juana

*Project Team*
Maximilian Reuss, Ana Paula Ruíz Galindo

*Acknowledgements*
DUCO Laboratorio de Diseño, José Juan Santa María, Precisión en Cortes Lasser, Andrés de la Rosa, Juan Carlos Perea García, Vero&Angel, Cushing

# PEDRO REYES
## *Mexico City, Mexico*
## People's United Nations: *pUN*

CHICAGO CULTURAL CENTER

*People's United Nations* is an experimental conference that seeks to apply techniques and resources from social psychology, theater, art, and conflict resolution to geopolitics. While the United Nations is comprised of career diplomats, *pUN* brings together 193 regular citizens who live in and have familial connections to the nations represented at the UN.

Over the course of a weekend, national representatives grapple with a set of hypothetical global proposals that seem advanced beyond the present, but which must be addressed. Although the proposals are often presented using the language of science fiction, they represent real issues at stake today.

Rather than a model version or a critique of the existing United Nations, *pUN*'s approach draws on the spirit of imagination and play to allow participants to engage in subjects whose magnitude is otherwise overwhelming.

The first general assembly of pUN took place in 2013 at Queens Museum in New York City; the second in early 2015 at the Hammer Museum in Los Angeles; a third edition is scheduled for late 2015 in Kanazawa, Japan.

*Project Team*
At least one representative of each nation-state on the planet

*Acknowledgements*
Larissa Harris, Queens Museum, Hammer Museum, Anne Ellegood, Galería Labor, Lisson Gallery

67

# PIOVENEFABI + YELLOWOFFICE + STEFANO GRAZIANI
## *Milan, Italy*
## Durana (L1)

Tirana sits in a bowl shaped by the mountains that surround the city. From there, a valley declines slowly towards the coast of Durrës, opening into a larger plain. The entire Durana region, as the urban corridor connecting Tirana to Durrës is nowadays called, is defined by the strong infrastructural and natural lines that run through it (the road, the railway, and the Tiranë river), and it is framed by geographical elements —mountains, hills, and (artificial) lakes. As such, Durana presents itself as a canvas of disconnected ecologies—the urban hills, the foothill villages, the linear city in formation, the industrial strip, the inhabited agricultural plain, and the river shores.

The project considers the whole bandwidth of the valley, from the hills to the river, giving a new meaning to the territorial lines crossing it. Rather than performing as pure infrastructure, the road, the railway, and the rivers are opened up toward the new city. The expressway is turned into a permeable urban road, the outdated Tirana-Durrës railway is transformed into a metropolitan light railway, while the border of the Tiranë river becomes a linear park.

*Durana (L1)* aims to structure a new urban network through a series of connecting paths and collective spaces of different entity and size, bringing a new public life to Durana. Piovenefabi's proposal investigates three case studies, which start from the region's three artificial lakes and connect the different ecologies of Durana. These paths, which run transverse to the valley, propose a new direction of development through a series of punctual operations on the existing urban tissue. Detecting specific points and increasing their public quality, providing new connections and repairing old ones, are the basic interventions, which allow the Durana linear development to open up into a proper urban entity, forcing on it a new mental and physical network.

Zooming in on the architectural scale, the project proposes three pilot interventions—a market canopy as civic infrastructure, an open pavilion as a shared facility, and the lake as a playground—in order to test the city's potential, which is already there but needs to be activated.

*Project Team*
Francesco Airoldi, Francesca Benedetto, Lucjano Bojaxhiu, Carlotta Capobianco, Daniele Dematté, Ambra Fabi, Marta Maria Ferrari, Stefano Graziani, Aleksa Korolija, Elios Kovaci, Marta Lelli, Emilio Mossa, Vladimir Myrtezai, Giacomo Nava, Rais Petrela, Giovanni Piovene, Elisa Scussolin, Cecilia Semeraro (PIOVENEFABI, YellowOffice, Stefano Graziani, MIC, Archispace)

*Acknowledgements*
Atelier Albania

# PLAN:B ARQUITECTOS
## *Medellín, Colombia*
## Hollow Trunk

A hollow trunk isn't empty. Its exterior bark is a surface of diverse exchanges; its thickness, structure, and interior are full of vitality.

The *Hollow Trunk* is an installation that expresses this quality of permeability—the possibility of interchange, transfer, and gradation. Permeable or open architecture has a broad capacity for adaptability and, by means of its geometric and spatial order, accepts both transformation in time as well as interaction between people and the weather. Many different types of architecture contain diverse expressions of this concept—especially in the tropical regions, where the climatic conditions enable the most intense physical expression of permeability.

The exterior of the *Hollow Trunk* presents seven definitive perspectives on permeability in architecture, each of which is illustrated by one of seven public projects designed by Plan:b Arquitectos in neotropical South America. Absorbency is the ability to take in meteorological forces without the use of mechanical climate systems; Fluency favors the coexistence of diverse biotic communities; Flexibility consists of adaptable tectonic strategies; Availability takes advantage of spaces which can be used in unexpected ways, given constant climate conditions; Exchange expresses the close relationship between open forms and participatory action; Circularity connects architecture with its material and energy network; and Convergence advocates the merging of different technologies, rather than favoring a singular solution.

The *Hollow Trunk* is built of lightweight, recycled materials. The artisanal paper and the printed images on the structure's exterior express the atmosphere and everyday materials typical of the tropical Colombian ecosystem.

*Project Team*
Felipe Mesa, Federico Mesa, Carlos Blanco, Laura Kate Correa, Esteban Hincapié, Ana María Londoño, Maria Clara Osorio

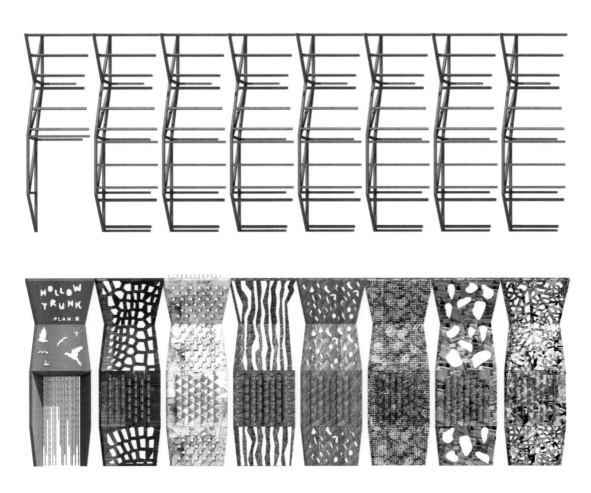

69

# POINT SUPREME
## *Athens, Greece*
## The Playfulness of the Real

The architecture of Point Supreme aims to reveal the hidden potential of a vibrant reality. Utopia does not need to refer to ideal, nonexistent cities — current cities can live in new ways. Point Supreme seek to stimulate broad public awareness of architecture through images that feed the collective subconscious and produce a new, public, critical imagination, proposing a new political role for the architect. Project compositions are playful and fun, drawing attention to the lack of optimism in contemporary architecture. They vary from radical to immediately realizable. Public space has a cultural role: it is a destination with identity and imagination.

Point Supreme's interrelated series of projects records the existing city of Athens with an obsessive attention to detail; buildings, squares, trees, lampposts, sunshades, and mountains are included with precision and become equal protagonists in the stories told. Ordinary objects are gathered without prejudice in a collection rich in tradition, history, and anonymous architecture. They are placed in synthesized oppositions, creating conditions for new relationships to develop. In contrast, the architecture is intentionally unalluring, to emphasize content and program over form. There are no preconceptions of scale or design disciplines—buildings are furniture, mountains are objects, and there is no difference between rooms and cities. The city becomes a systematically exploited experimental field.

*Project Team*
Marianna Rentzou, Konstantinos Pantazis

# PRODUCTORA
## *Mexico City, Mexico*
## Hotel Tulum

Hotel Tulum is a small ten-room boutique hotel built near the town of Tulum, not far from the well-known Mayan pyramids. Two independent Mexican hotel operators commissioned PRODUCTORA in 2007 to design a new hotel on a site already occupied by an abandoned one. The project had obtained building permits by the beginning of 2008, and construction started in February of that year. By the summer, the rough structure was almost fully realized, but political struggles between the municipal and federal governments closed down the building site. For several years, the project stood half-built next to the Caribbean Sea, waiting for lawyers, agents, and lobbyists to find a solution to the bureaucratic impasse. Plants and vegetation took over, plasterwork crumbled, people seeking shelter moved in and out, and of the project's initial intentions, only some ruins survived. Eventually, the clients sold the plot and the project was abandoned.

The brass model is a pristine formal composition: an abstract representation of Hotel Tulum, as if it were a new building to be presented to the public. The model—approximately 3 ft. (1 m) in diameter and realized in a single brass cast—embodies the ethos of a typical modernist project: a play of sculpture, form, and mass; a composition of abstract elements dispersed over the existing topography and built in a solid material confirming its value and timelessness.

The counterpart of this idealized appearance is an audio-visual montage based on photographic material shot around 2013. A voiceover provides commentary over a set of thirty-one slides of the now-decayed hotel. The images used are simple snapshots taken by another architecture office (Studio Arquitectos) that was commissioned to build over the ruins of PRODUCTORA's project. Recalling the classical narratives of Mexican history, layer upon layer of spatial proposals and architectural intentions are superimposed. In the film, the narrator alternates between describing what we see in these images and exploring visions of what might have been. The austere sadness of the projected images stands in stark contrast to the evocative design process for an unlikely future.

*Project Team*
Wonne Ickx, Victor Jaime, Carlos Bedoya Ikeda, Abel Perles, with Iñaki Bonillas

*Acknowledgements*
Juan Luis Rivera, Eduardo Garcia, Paulina Villa (Studio Arquitectos)

Image: Studio Arquitectos

# RAAAF (RIETVELD ARCHITECTURE-ART-AFFORDANCES)
## *Amsterdam, The Netherlands*
## The End of Sitting – Cut Out

Image: Jan Kempenaers

*The End of Sitting – Cut Out* is an installation at the crossroads of architecture, visual art, and philosophy. In our society, the near entirety of our surroundings has been designed for sitting, but evidence from medical research suggests that sitting for too long is unhealthy. RAAAF has developed a concept wherein the chair and desk are no longer unquestionable starting points. Instead, the installation's various "affordances" (possibilities of action) solicit visitors to explore different positions from that iteration and to move dynamically in an experimental working landscape. *The End of Sitting – Cut Out* marks the beginning of an experimental trial phase, exploring the possibilities for a radical change in the way we will work in offices in 2025.

This installation is a follow-up to one that RAAAF and Barbara Visser built in Amsterdam. It is cut out of the previous landscape of standing affordances, including the most successful positions. It allows visitors to stand, lean, hang, or lay down while interacting, reading, or working.

*Project Team*
Ronald Rietveld, Erik Rietveld, Arna Mackic, David Habets, Bastiaan Bervoets, Denis Bacal (RAAAF); Koos Schaart, Koen van Oort, Jerzy Planting (Schaart Adventures)

*Acknowledgements*
Concept developed in collaboration with visual artist Barbara Visser and supported by Looiersgracht 60 (Soraya Notoadikusumo and Nadine Snijders) in Amsterdam. Installation produced with financial support from the Netherlands Organisation for Scientific Research (NWO), Creative Industry Fund NL, and The Art of Impact.

# RAMAK FAZEL
## *Claremont / San Francisco, US*
## Sectional City

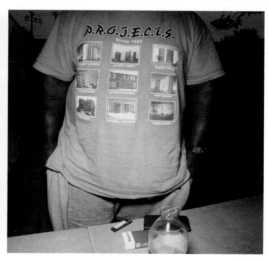

What does the diversity of life on city streets reveal? Can a deeper engagement with what is "seen"—scratching beneath the surface—result in a more nuanced understanding of human commonalities? The distinct characteristics of Chicago's streets function as a gateway into a multitude of realities where shared values bind human experience.

*Sectional City* attempts to question the myth of Chicago as a coherent architectural and urban creation. Maps have historically sectioned Chicago into convenient socioeconomic sectors and neighborhood classifications. Deliberately drawn lines determined the patterns of votes cast, taxes paid, and mail delivered. Computational geocoding further promoted a more narrow reading, often overemphasizing economic metrics. But such mapping strategies can have detrimental and often inescapable effects. By definition, they rarely cast light on the intrepid human qualities that function as a social connective tissue.

Fazel's work is a consistent formal photographic and methodological approach to presenting the subject in a nonhierarchical way. This series of photographs is informed by personal interactions and neighborly conversations. The images suggest an alternative overlay onto the existing urban gradient, placing human relations in greater focus. Never perfect, convenient, or tidy, *Sectional City* underscores the idea that contradictory observations can generate poetic meaning where intractable ideological differences collapse.

*Acknowledgements*
Jade Boudreaux, Jialuo Wu, and the numerous
Chicagoans who extended a collective warm welcome

# RUA ARQUITETOS
## *Rio de Janeiro, Brazil*
## Cultural Territory:
## Complexo da Maré

Whether represented as territories of violence or inventiveness, usual views of *favelas* stigmatize and reinforce the idea of an independent urban entity that is separated from the rest of the city. Through much of their past and current work, RUA seeks to disrupt these representations.

Maré is a large flat area in the North Zone of Rio de Janeiro that is home to about 130,000 people, distributed among more than 30,000 small buildings, each often up to three floors. It is located amid the main highways of the city, and its size and population are comparable to Copacabana. At first glance a single and homogeneous favela, it is actually made up of sixteen neighborhoods with particular historical processes and present challenges.

In 2011, RUA was invited by the local organization Observatório de Favelas and art producer Automática to plan the renovation of an old warehouse at the fringes of one of Maré's neighborhoods, transforming it into the Bela Maré Art Center, and to design exhibitions for the Travessias arts initiative, which takes place in Maré once a year. Now in its fourth edition, the event proposes the incorporation of Maré in the map of visual arts, emphasizing its role in the process of territorial and aesthetic integration. Through exhibitions that combine the best Brazilian contemporary artists, local initiatives, and workshops, this arts initiative aims to facilitate a flow of people and ideas, repositioning Maré in the context of the larger city.

Inspired by the vision of Observatório de Favelas, the renovation design for the warehouse proposes the addition of a tower, a vertical landmark in a horizontal landscape, establishing a series of territorial and symbolic relations. In parallel to the design work, RUA built an incremental, large-scale model, made of small wooden blocks, to represent the whole Maré area, as an invitation for ideas and a platform for conversations. The model has been growing and transforming since 2013.

*Project Team*
Pedro Évora, Pedro Rivera, Fabiano Pires

*Acknowledgements*
Observatório de Favelas, Automática Produções Artísticas

# RURAL URBAN FRAMEWORK
## *Hong Kong, China*
## Rural Collage: Strategies for the Chinese Countryside

How do we design for rapidly developing and ever-changing contexts? Can we replace the mantra of "built to last" with "built to adapt"? Building in areas of uncertain transformation calls for a design approach that embraces contradiction as a strategic response.

In 2005, China's eleventh five-year plan proposed a significant shift of focus from cities to the countryside, speculating that, during the following two decades, 350 million rural citizens would become urbanized. At the same time, Rural Urban Framework began to work in Qinmo, a small rural village in the Guangdong Province, developing a series of projects as strategic responses to the pressure of urbanization and the subsequent adjustments to rural livelihood.

Since then, Rural Urban Framework has continued researching and building projects in over twenty such sites in China. It has resolved the collisions between small-scale and large-scale infrastructure, applying both top-down and bottom-up strategies, inserting "alien" programs, and adapting to local contexts. Its tactics reflect the multiple conflicts that have arisen through the urbanization process. Ten years on, Rural Urban Framework's projects both reveal and contribute to the complex, paradoxical nature of rapid urbanization.

The result is a toolbox of strategies, with the goal of a clearer understanding of the rural-urban transformation. Rural Urban Framework's work has been organized as a series of five debates: Individual Prototype vs. Collective Design, Incremental Planning vs. Instant Urbanism, Site-Specific vs. Generic Construction, Micro Insertion vs. Macro Infrastructure, Programmatic Mutation vs. Spatial Adaptation. Each pair of themes is illustrated through a direct design experience.

The ten projects that were chosen illustrate the necessity for architects to adopt multifaceted approaches to developing regions. Rather than thinking of architecture as a fixed solution to a stable site, architects can give it a key role in the process of transformation.

*Project Team*
Joshua Bolchover, John Lin (directors); Eva Herunter (project leader); Akshara Khaitan, Bo Yee Lau, Kevin Lin, Paul Mok, Justin Yeung, Jonathan Pang Tin Yui, Thet Htoo Zin; Rural Urban Framework is a research and design lab at the University of Hong Kong

# SELGASCANO + HELLOEVERYTHING
## *Madrid, Spain / New York City, US*
## Casa A

*Casa A* tests an array of building enclosures. The different materials cooperate through a common structure to generate a prototypical prefabricated dwelling. The project exemplifies two parallel veins of design research, which operate as a common whole.

The prototype uses industry standards in affordable fabrication to develop a structural system to which customized enclosure elements can be attached. The cladding expands the palette of unexplored material assemblies that may be applied to an architectural enclosure.

The result is a highly versatile transformer, using the spatial flexibility of its construction to generate a range of tectonic and atmospheric conditions. Integrating prefabricated construction systems with unique prototypical material studies, *Casa A* foregrounds a playful synthesis of standard and custom design systems instrumental to an adaptable architecture.

*Project Team*
Jose Selgas, Lucia Cano, Julian Ocampo,
Austin Smith, Sixto Cordero

# SMOUT ALLEN +
# GEOFF MANAUGH
*London, UK / New York City, US*
# LA Recalculated

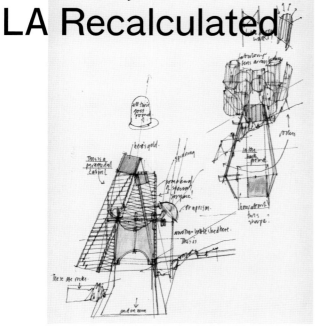

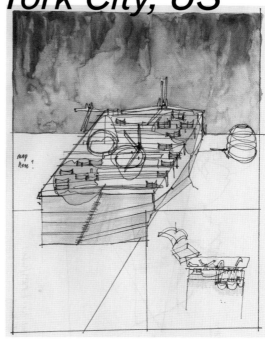

Los Angeles is a city where natural history, aerospace research, astronomical observation, and the planetary sciences hold outsized urban influence. From the risk of catastrophic earthquakes to the region's still-operational oil fields, from its long history of military aviation to its complex relationship with migratory wildlife, Los Angeles is not just a megacity. Its ecological fragility, combined with a dangerous lack of terrestrial stability, means that Los Angeles requires continual monitoring and study: from its creeks to its summits, the city has been ornamented with scientific equipment, crowned with electromagnetic antennae, and ringed with seismic stations, transforming it into an urban-scale research facility, a living device inhabited by millions of people on the continent's westernmost edge.

The cartographic drawing — part map, part plan, part deep section — takes conceptual inspiration from the book *OneFiveFour* by Lebbeus Woods. There, Woods describes a hypothetical city shaped by the existential threat of seismic events surging through the ground below. In order to understand how this unstable ground might undermine the metropolis, the city has augmented itself on nearly every surface, Woods writes, with "oscilloscopes, refractors, seismometers, interferometers, and other, as yet unknown instruments, measuring light, movement, force, change." In this city of instruments — this city *as* instrument—"tools for extending perceptivity to all scales of nature are built spontaneously, playfully, experimentally, continuously modified in home laboratories, in laboratories that are homes," exploring the moving surface of an Earth in flux. Architecture becomes a means for giving shape to these existential investigations.

Twenty-first-century Los Angeles has inadvertently fulfilled Woods's speculative vision. It is less a city, in some ways, than it is a matrix of seismic equipment and geological survey tools used for locating, mapping, and mitigating the effects of tectonic faults. This permanent flux and lack of anchorage makes Los Angeles *bathymetric,* rather than terrestrial. The city is also a graveyard of leftover physics experiments that once measured and established the speed of light, using prisms, mirrors, and interferometers in the San Gabriel Mountains (an experiment now marked by historic plaques and Piranesian obelisks). Los Angeles is also home to the Griffith and Mt. Wilson Observatories, through which the city achieved its often-overlooked but vital role in the history of global astronomy. Finally, it incorporates a carefully studied nest of wildlife traps and ecological monitoring stations designed to track species other than human as they infiltrate, settle, and partially colonize the built environment.

Seen through the lens of this expanded context, Los Angeles becomes an archipelago of scientific instruments often realized at the scale of urban infrastructure: densely inhabited, with one eye on the stars, sliding out of alignment with itself, and jostled from below by seismic tides.

*Project Team*
Laura Allen, Geoff Manaugh, Mark Smout

*Acknowledgements*
Andrew Barrington, Harry Grocott, Doug Miller, Sandra Youkhana; Additional support from the USC Libraries Discovery Fellowship, the Bartlett School of Architecture, UCL, and the British Council

# SO–IL
## *New York City, US*
## Passage

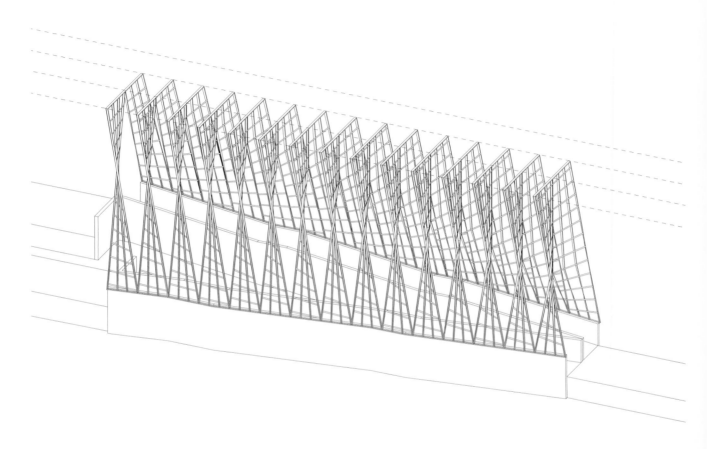

*Passage* reflects upon the spatial qualities of the ramp. An inclined plane destabilizes; as a connection of horizontal planes, the ramp is ambiguous and inherently in-between. At once an opportunity for disruption and an apparatus for universal access to space, the ramp as an architectural device has been the subject of extensive design and theoretical speculation. But how do we experience being on a ramp? Movement is clearly directional, up or down.

More than a staircase, the subtle change in grade affects one's sense of self. One realizes one's own physical being, one's body mass. The body corrects our movement, adjusting pace and posture in response to the ramp's incline and length. *Passage* aims to disrupt this ingrained response, as if to heighten one's awareness of space.

SO-IL's project consists of a series of portals that envelop the ramp in the Chicago Cultural Center, each of them in a different shape. Seen from a distance, the structure increases the volumetric presence of the ramp; but walking through it, the sequence of portals unfolds like individual picture frames that give pace to one's movement. The repetition of frames alternately slows down or accelerates the sense of movement through the space. Their varied heights shift the perception of perspective.

The installation is made of standard off-the-shelf steel studs, an omnipresent architectural material that is rarely visible, usually hidden behind layers of sheetrock and insulation. Daylight entering the space through two large glazed openings highlights the reflective surface of the portals and the individual presence of the frames.

*Project Team*
Florian Idenburg, Jing Liu, Ilias Papageorgiou, Lucie Rebeyrol, Pietro Pagliaro

# SOU FUJIMOTO ARCHITECTS
## *Tokyo, Japan*
## Architecture Is Everywhere

One of the key ideas behind Sou Fujimoto's practice is that architecture is first found and then made. Just as our ancestors found their habitat in caves and woods, we discover ours among the many things we encounter in the immense urban jungle.

The notion of "found architecture" is represented by juxtaposing human figures and ordinary objects found in everyday life with contexts that might seem coincidental at first, if not fortuitous. This operation makes us start to read these objects as architectural spaces. While we might find these serendipitous pairings interesting for their discrepancy in scale, what lies beyond them might well be the prelude to a new architecture.

Fujimoto's approach can be traced back to Marcel Duchamp's readymades or John Cage's series of chance operations — specifically, the act of discovering by chance rather than creating with intent. *Architecture Is Everywhere* aims to radically question the boundary between "found" and "made" architecture.

*Project Team*
Sou Fujimoto, Masaki Iwata, Toshiyuki Nakagawa, Minako Suzuki, Hugh Hsu

79

# STEFANO BOERI ARCHITETTI
## *Milan, Italy*
## The Flying Gardeners

Photo: Laura Cionci, The BlinkFish

Ugo always chews gum. Gilberto wears a scarf. Massimo has dreadlocks. Every four months, they fly around the forest. They hang on ropes from the edge of the roof and descend, jumping from balcony to balcony, to prune dead branches, thin out leaves if they are too unbalanced, check the health of the trees. They studied botany and then learned how to become climbers. And now there they are, gardeners floating in the sky of Milan, appearing and disappearing in the frame of the large windows; they slide along the trunks in lateral moves and vertical lines.

Only botanists and climbers are conscious of the richness of life in the Vertical Forest. While taking care of the trees, they have learned to observe human lives in a sequence of intimate frames: furniture, paintings on the wall, and dirty dishes become evidence of the life of a couple, or of a family. These are the clues that the flying detectives collect, observing, from behind the leaves, the anger, calm, boredom, sex, and loneliness of a vertical humanity—stories for a kind of vegetal psychoanalysis.

The *Bosco Verticale* residential towers were designed by Stefano Boeri, Gianandrea Barreca, and Giovanni La Varra, and completed in 2014.

*Project Team*
Stefano Boeri (artistic director); Azzurra Muzzonigro (curator); The BlinkFish (film production); Giacomo Boeri, Matteo Grimaldi (film directors)

*Acknowledgements*
Francesca Parvizyar; Azimut SGR; Solidea; Istituto Nazionale per il Commercio Estero (Comune di Milano)

# STUDIO [D] TALE
## *Harare, Zimbabwe / Cape Town, South Africa / London, UK*
## Dollar Vans

Studio [D] Tale is designing a map for the transit network in Harare, Zimbabwe. Presently, in spite of the care taken by the state and local authorities to regulate the estimated 4,500 individual operators registered as commuter-omnibus owners, passengers have a difficult time navigating freely throughout their city. *Dollar Vans* is a means to offer the conveniences of a route map and way-finding signs. Studio [D] Tale hopes to allow people to get to know their city so that they may discover new neighborhoods through the intervention of low-cost, community-based designs and research.

Harare is a sprawling conurbation with just over two million inhabitants who rely on a network of independent owner-operated minibuses to get to and from home, work, or school. Each minibus ferries at most twenty-six seated passengers at one time. These minibuses are ubiquitous in every African city, from Cape Town to Cairo. As a consequence, *Dollar Vans* considers that grand urban transit projects are a distant reality for most cities on the continent and is focused on designing a solution for this most prevalent mode of transport. Most African cities cannot wait to have their own Gautrain, the high-speed railway built in 2010 in Johannesburg.

However, ever since Medellín, Colombia, opened its urban cable car system, Metrocable, for $26 million in 2004, social urbanization—a movement to include previously marginalized communities in the development of cities—has gained favor in many town halls. Even established transit networks are addressing failings in their networks that have left some in their cities deprived of good access to public services—the City of Chicago has been trying to close major gaps in its transit system since 2011 with a $4 billion investment.

In the past, Harare was indeed serviced by the parastatal company Zimbabwe United Passenger Company (ZUPCO). At its peak ZUPCO had over 1,200 buses operating 426 routes. In the late 1990s, the company's operations suffered heavily as a result of mismanagement and the deregulation of the transport sector in favor of owner-operated commuter minibuses that were common in the rest of Africa. The introduction of these minibuses was also seen as a way to promote self-employment in Zimbabwe. Now, in the absence of the state-run buses, Harare relies on the community of private minibuses.

Studio [D] Tale's research team has been gathering information from school children and professionals who commute daily in and out of the city. Minibus drivers have also been sharing their route information. These regular users and volunteers have helped ensure that *Dollar Vans* reflects the situation on the ground.

*Project Team*
Maxwell Mutanda, Safia Qureshi, Getrude Mufanebadza, Kudzayi Mwashita, Rutendo Dube, Ruth Marere, Wonderful Chikandamina

*Acknowledgements*
Ministry of Transport, Zimbabwe; Department of Works, City of Harare

# STUDIO ALBORI
## *Milan, Italy*
# Makeshift

*Makeshift* is an exploration of the themes of reuse and improvisation in architecture. It deals with these universal subjects by starting from a local dimension—that of two cultures rooted in the United States, and particularly in Chicago.

In the construction industry, the culture of reuse spread widely in North American cities during the recent recession. A large number of new organizations for the reuse of building materials are giving rise to a practice that strengthens civic values and everyday sustainability, in contrast with the predominant consumerist ideology. But for now, this practice of reuse is a social phenomenon more than an architectural one: architectural culture is yet to be shaken by this (very old) novelty at a depth commensurate with the environmental crisis.

The culture of improvisation is also something that crosses all periods and fields of human activity. In the field of music, Chicago has been a cradle for this culture. It was here that such masters as Louis Armstrong and Sun Ra developed important parts of their work, and that the world-renowned Association for the Advancement of Creative Music flourished.

Beyond music, improvisation has, until very recent times, been a fundamental component in the practice of popular architecture and in the making of human habitat. At some point, it was considered synonymous with underdevelopment and so eradicated from modern and contemporary architecture praxis and ultimately confined to artistic or authorial practices. Improvisation is about making decisions according to the present time and place. The current prevalence of a culture of remote control, drying up the dialectic between preplanning and improvising, has established an environment in which the sense of place disappears—bodily substance replaced by a sum of information.

The adjective "makeshift" brings the categories of reuse and improvisation together. It implies an action completed with what is available at any given moment. *Makeshift* is a construction built exclusively with materials available in the warehouses of Chicago-based reuse organizations. At the end of the Biennial, it will be dismantled and its components returned to the warehouses to be sold. *Makeshift* provides a place where visitors can rest for a moment, and at the same time where musicians can improvise their performances.

*Project Team*
Emanuele Almagioni, Giacomo Borella, Francesca Riva; Carlo Micheletti (Micheletti Ingegneria, Brescia)

*Acknowledgments*
Rebuilding Exchange, Chicago

# STUDIO GANG
## *Chicago, US*
## Polis Station

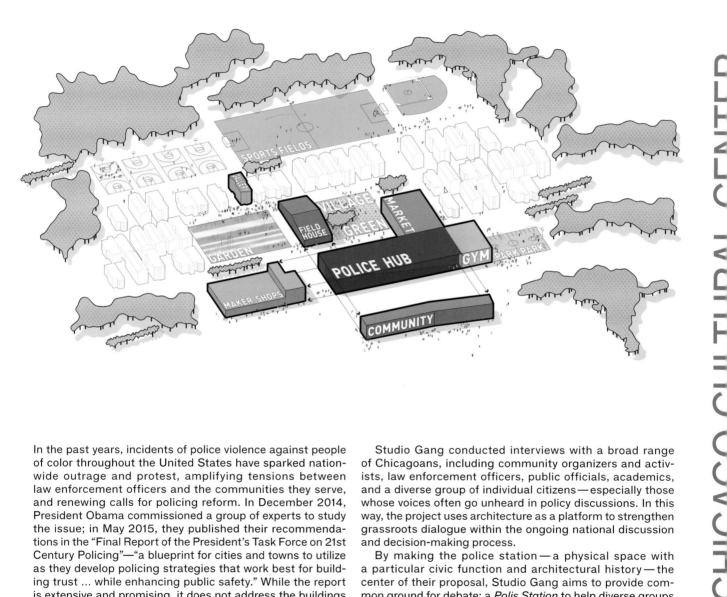

In the past years, incidents of police violence against people of color throughout the United States have sparked nationwide outrage and protest, amplifying tensions between law enforcement officers and the communities they serve, and renewing calls for policing reform. In December 2014, President Obama commissioned a group of experts to study the issue; in May 2015, they published their recommendations in the "Final Report of the President's Task Force on 21st Century Policing"—"a blueprint for cities and towns to utilize as they develop policing strategies that work best for building trust ... while enhancing public safety." While the report is extensive and promising, it does not address the buildings that are used for policing or of their potential to help usher in the changes that are urgently sought.

Recognizing the significance of this crossroads moment, Studio Gang began to investigate how the spatial and physical environment of the police station might be reimagined in order to help build a more just and trusting relationship between citizens and police. *Polis Station* is conceived as a supplement to the task force's report. Translating the architects' research and community engagement process into speculative design, it is meant to stimulate a new strand of productive conversations on policing and its future.

Studio Gang conducted interviews with a broad range of Chicagoans, including community organizers and activists, law enforcement officers, public officials, academics, and a diverse group of individual citizens—especially those whose voices often go unheard in policy discussions. In this way, the project uses architecture as a platform to strengthen grassroots dialogue within the ongoing national discussion and decision-making process.

By making the police station—a physical space with a particular civic function and architectural history—the center of their proposal, Studio Gang aims to provide common ground for debate: a *Polis Station* to help diverse groups of stakeholders from across the country to envision how policing could improve in their own communities.

*Project Team*
Jeanne Gang, Mark Schendel, Gia Biagi, Laura Ettedgui, Emily Licht, Chris Bennett, Sarah Kramer, Alissa Anderson, Juan de la Mora, Schuyler Smith

# TATIANA BILBAO S.C.
## *Mexico City, Mexico*
## Sustainable Housing

> Every family has the right to enjoy decent housing.
> The law establishes the tools and support necessary
> to achieve that objective.
> —*Constitución Política de los Estados Unidos Mexicanos*

Social housing has become one of the most important issues on the present-day architectural agenda. There are more than thirty million houses in Mexico, but, with a total population of about 120 million and one of the highest population growth rates in Latin America, the country's housing shortage amounts to a total of nine million homes.

Within this panorama, Tatiana Bilbao developed a project whose most important objective is to create a housing prototype with good spatial and material qualities at an affordable price. To achieve such a goal, it was necessary to know what the prospective tenants would need in terms of materials, form, function, and appearance. After several in situ interviews and workshops—in contrast with the bulk of social housing being built around the country—they arrived at a design that adopts the form of an archetypical house (a pitched roof), while adapting to geographic, social, and cultural variations.

Tatiana Bilbao expanded the minimal federal requirement of 463 sq. ft. (43 m²) per house by building a central core of rigid materials (concrete blocks) and surrounding modules of lighter and cheaper materials (wooden pallets). These allow the homes to be expanded in phases, adapting to each family's budget and desires, while preserving the outside appearance of a completed house. The first phase of the house includes two bedrooms, one bathroom, one kitchen, and a 16 ft. (5 m) high dining and living room. When completed, the third phase will provide space for five separate bedrooms.

The architects used several technological solutions in order to achieve maximum energy efficiency. A number of different interior arrangements were developed to cope with varying urban and rural habits and traditions, creating a possibility for Mexican families to live in an appropriate and dignified house.

*Project Team*
Tatiana Bilbao, David Vaner, Catia Bilbao (master plan and architecture); Juan Pablo Benlliure (office manager); Alba Cortés (team leader); Sonia Castañón, Valentina Marchetti, Enrique Silva, Abelardo Bravo, Alejandro Campos, Karen Díaz de León (design team)

# TOMA
## *Santiago, Chile*
# Especulopolis

SOCIALIST UTOPIAS · CITY RUINS AND LEGACY · DETERIORATION OF PUBLIC HOUSING · EL LADRILLO (THE BRICK) · MILITARY DICTATORSHIP CHILE · SPECULATIVE CITY · PRIVATIZATION OF PUBLIC SERVICES · NEOLIBERAL ECONOMICS THEORIES · CHICAGO BOYS (CHILE) · THE BRIGADE · ACTIVATIONS · THE INSTITUTIONS · MANIFESTATIONS OF NEOLIBERAL POLICIES / SANTIAGO CITY · SANTIAGO CITY AS A LABORATORY · THE NEOLIBERAL EXPERIMENT · GENERIC CITIES · SEGREGATION OF THE CITY · UNIVERSITY OF CHICAGO · DEREGULATION OF URBAN LIMITS · TERRITORIAL FORENSIC INVESTIGATION

How to write a manifesto in an age that is saturated with them? If the weakness of manifestos is their inherent lack of evidence, the vital power of speculation rests on its capacity to construct alternative realities. The city of Santiago is a place where two different modes of speculation can come together: the archaeologist's speculation, which reconstructs the traces of other cities that could have been, and the detective's speculation, which connects the evidence of previous crimes.

Santiago is a hub of urban stories. Its streets and buildings reflect layers of past occupations, abandoned projects, truncated fantasies, monumental delusions, and community organizations.

Since the 1960s, a new culture—the culture of speculation—chose Santiago as its laboratory: a city isolated between the longest mountain range and the largest ocean became a place to invent and test new urban models.

TOMA proposes a history of speculation in the contemporary city through a number of case studies: a 1960s social housing project in Santiago's wealthiest district, which has become the city's main financial center; an early twentieth-century hat factory being transformed into an innovation hub; a formerly popular cultural center that later became the seat of the military government, and has now reclaimed its original function, though in a less popular way; the unfinished structure of what was to become Latin America's biggest hospital, now being turned into storage space; a vast area with public housing and an abandoned factory, on the agenda of corporate cultural transformation.

*Especulopolis* takes the idea of an urban laboratory as the foundation for a collective experiment to build a manifesto for Santiago. Through an investigation of the city, its history, and futures, TOMA aims to give apparently discontinuous—or even irreconcilable—episodes a new degree of coherence, making Santiago a city from which others can learn.

*Project Team*
Eduardo Pérez, Ignacio Saavedra, Leandro Cappetto, Ignacio Rivas, Mathias Klenner

# TOMÁS SARACENO
## *Berlin, Germany*

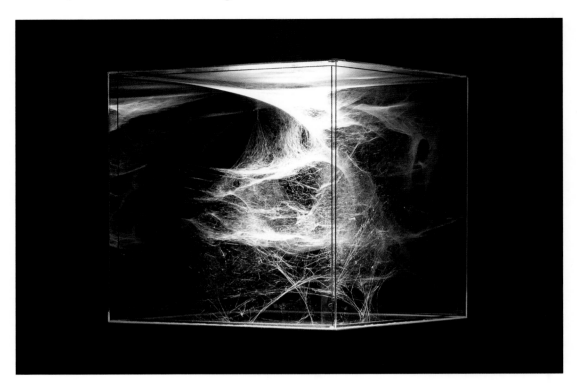

Photo: Courtesy of the artist and Tanya Bonakdar Gallery, New York

*Semi-social musical instrument Arp 77: built by a single Cyrtophora Moluccensis—one week*

*Hybrid solitary semi-social musical instrument Ophiuchus: built by Parasteatoda Lunata—two weeks—and a Cyrtophora Citricola—two weeks*

*Hybrid solitary semi-social musical instrument NGC 660: built by one Nephila Clavipes—two weeks—one Argiope Anasuj—two weeks—and a pair of Cyrtophora Citricola—two weeks*

*Hybrid solitary semi-social musical instrument Arp 87: built by a couple of Cyrtophora Citricola—one month—one Agelena Labyrinthica—two months—one Cyrtophora Moluccensis—two weeks—and one Tegenria Domestica—four months (turned four times 180 degrees on Z axis)*

Saraceno's multidisciplinary artistic practice takes inspiration from a variety of sources, including architecture, space exploration, science fiction, and geometries found in the biological sciences. Among these subjects, Saraceno has long included arachnology as a tool for the investigation of alternative constructions, forming the basis for several recent exhibitions. For Saraceno, spider webs spark inquiry into possible modes of redefining relationships between humans and nature, proposing utopian conditions for sustainable societies.

When entering into Saraceno's installation, a visitor's perception is reoriented in a darkened environment dotted with glowing sculptures that are articulated in silvery spider silk. Formed of complex interwoven geometries suspended in air, each piece appears as a unique galaxy floating within an expansive, infinite landscape. The works' titles reveal the technical basis for each sculptural element, like the genus and species of the spider collaborators and the amount of time needed to construct their webs. During the building period of a sculpture, each cube is turned onto its different sides, dislodging gravity and interweaving concepts of freedom and control within the work. The product of this action is reminiscent of the object-cum-constellation Ophiuchus, referred to in one of the titles. And yet the objects themselves defy the framework of their titles, as the intricate web formations in each cube neither belong to human logic nor are something that would exist in nature.

### Project Team
Tomás Saraceno, Adrian Krell, Lars Behrendt, Joshua Hoareau, Sofia Lemos, Vero Lugaro, Claudia Melendez, Ignas Petronis, Serena Rota, Javier Rosenberg, Daniel Schulz, Christophe Vaillant

### Acknowledgements
Peter Jäger (Senckenberg Research Institute, Frankfurt am Main); Samuel Zschokke (University of Basel); Yael Lubin (president of the International Society of Arachnology –Jakob Blaustein Institutes for Desert Research, Israel); Center for Art, Science and Technology, Massachusetts Institute of Technology; Tanya Bonakdar Gallery, New York; Andersen's Contemporary, Copenhagen; Pinksummer Contemporary Art, Genoa; Esther Schipper Gallery, Berlin

# URBZ
## *Mumbai, India*
## Homegrown Homes

Many of Mumbai's service providers, manual workers, and self-employed people live in neighborhoods that emerged generations ago. They have ad hoc occupancy rights wherever possible, but most find themselves living with insecure tenancy. Whether they are designated as slums or urban villages, or are as yet uncategorized, these habitats have grown largely through the efforts of the residents themselves, with the help of local construction artisans who specialize in small homes. The settlements suffer as much from a breakdown of concepts, vocabulary, and perception as from the malfunctioning of the administration and limited access to resources.

At the heart of the physical life of Shivaji Nagar and other resident-built neighborhoods in Mumbai is the relationship of the resident and the builder. This equation is a key part of urbz's engagement with urban issues in Mumbai, as it believes that architects can only be relevant in these neighborhoods when they engage directly with local actors.

*Homegrown Homes* showcases the story of one particular house, which urbz designed together with a local contractor, architects, and engineers. The intervention was aimed at bringing together people who live in parallel professional worlds and who have different ways of imagining and building the city. The project also highlights the knowhow that exists in Shivaji Nagar and presents local expertise as a central part of any planned development strategy.

While the construction was fast and without major problems, negotiating between the architects' intentions, local realities, the architectural design, and fuzzy regulations proved more complex.

The house was built in two stages and is likely to be modified again in the future. Urbz first built a 14 ft. (4 m) high structure, which adhered to the height limit imposed by the government for construction in "slum areas." When this regulation changed a few months later, the team increased the height of the building.

Video documentation of that process provides a glimpse of the travails and triumphs of most of the homegrown homes of this kind that make up the settlement at large. The process of construction, the design, the post-occupancy experiences, and the reconstruction of certain parts encompass the entire gamut of experiences typical of such a process. *Homegrown Homes* is a microcosm of a larger experience, which complicates the representation of neighborhoods that are usually dismissed as Mumbai's slum problem.

By focusing on local agency in the physical growth of the settlement—both at the level of a home as well as the neighborhood as a whole—urbz seeks to demonstrate that such processes have structure, organization, and a financial logic that cannot be ignored under cover of euphemisms such as "informal" or "unorganized."

*Project Team*
Rahul Srivastava, Matias Echanove, Jai Bhadgaonkar, Ketaki Tare, Bharat Gangurde, Apoorva Tadepalli, Rishi Chandna

*Acknowledgements*
The house residents; Pankaj Gupta, local builder, and his team; sP+a architects

# VO TRONG NGHIA ARCHITECTS
## *Ho Chi Minh City, Vietnam*
# S HOUSE

According to the statistics, the total housing area in Vietnam has increased tenfold in the last decade. However, many families still live in small houses, some less than 107 sq. ft. (10 m²). People in the Mekong Delta, on an average income of less than $130 per month, mainly live in temporary houses. Ironically, poor-quality structures result in high maintenance costs. Therefore, low-cost but permanent, quickly built but high-quality housing is an urgent social demand in the region.

Against this backdrop, VTN has developed *S HOUSE*, a serial project for low-income households in the Mekong Delta area. After the building of three prototypes in South Vietnam, *S HOUSE* is now moving toward the mass-production phase while trying to expand overseas.

The key features of the house are fast construction, durability, affordability, easy transportation, flexibility, and possibilities for customization. The complete structure can be assembled in three hours. The prefabricated elements need minimal assembly on site, while lightweight materials and the use of a dry-joint system allow all construction to be done without power tools or skilled labor.

The life span of the building is estimated to be more than thirty years. All building elements are industrially manufactured to ensure durability, and all steel is galvanized to prevent rusting. The supporting structure has a longer life, while the skin of the house is detachable and can be replaced.

Each unit costs less than $4,000, mainly because the building elements are manufactured in large numbers. The house's slender design and sectional shape bring down material costs, and the choice of local materials makes finishing less expensive. Residents are encouraged to participate in the assembly of their home, to reduce the cost of construction.

Each component weighs less than 130 lb. (60 kg), so they can be transported by hand. The modules of *S HOUSE* were designed keeping the standard dimensions of containers in mind for international shipping.

*S HOUSE* responds to local needs in terms of its finishing materials, and can include insulation if the climate demands it. An open floor plan enables flexibility in usage, and the modular system allows for future additions to the space. This means that the *S HOUSE* could also be used as a school, office, community center, emergency shelter, or as a possible alternative to slums.

The first two prototypes of *S HOUSE* were built in Dong Nai and the Mekong Delta in Vietnam, in 2014, and VTN is working to develop even lighter and cheaper versions.

*Project Team*
Vo Trong Nghia, Masaaki Iwamoto, Kosuke Nishijima, So Adachi; Wind and Water House JSC

# WAI ARCHITECTURE THINK TANK
## *Beijing, China*
# Narrative Architecture: A Manifesto

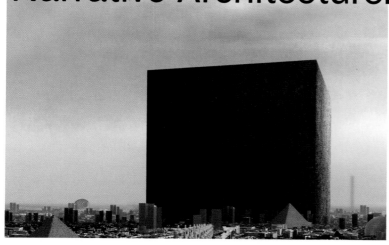

There is a form of architecture that aims at not getting built: an architecture on paper that should not be confused with paper architecture. An architecture based on pure statements in which real brick, mortar, and poured concrete are substituted by cut-and-pasted paper and narrative prose. An architecture about the failed and accomplished ambitions of buildings and master plans. An architecture which, although focused on the critique of this ambition, is not concerned with just any form of critique. An architecture not preoccupied with the critic's view in newspapers, with the comments on populist design blogs, nor with the propaganda centerfolds of glossy magazines. An architecture that talks directly to architecture about architecture. An architecture of disciplinary struggle.

This form of architecture focuses on the critique of ideology, after recognizing that ideology—in its multiple incarnations—has infiltrated all spheres of architectural production, including the sphere of criticism itself. Through narrative texts and a vast repertoire of images (collages, photomontages, drawings, storyboards, comic strips, and animations), this architecture creates allegorical stories that aim to expose the impasses and misfires of architecture in theory and practice. This form of architecture is simultaneously both theory and practice. It is theory as practice; critique as architectural project. We call it Narrative Architecture, and this project presents a display of its potential as a tool for the development of a critical discourse of contemporary architecture.

The project presents four fantastic scenarios, each one performing a different critique of architectural ideology by integrating allegorical texts with still and moving images and sound, highlighting architectural ambitions, failures, and potentialities with irony and humor.

In a continuous spatial layout, each project is presented through different modes of representation including text, film, collages, and prints, as well as large-scale models and artifacts. Conceived as a total installation, the public forms an integral component, not only in its interaction with the showcased projects but also in the possibility of participating in events and happenings to create new Narrative Architecture projects.

*Project Team*
Cruz García, Nathalie Frankowski

# WOLFF ARCHITECTS
## *Cape Town, South Africa*
## Halo

"Design something the world will never forget. Something that will be associated with Cape Town forever after. Something temporary." That was the brief that Wolff Architects received for a structure to celebrate Cape Town as the World Design Capital in 2014.

The response was a halo of light, 330 ft. (100 m) in diameter, that would appear at night above Lion's Head, a mountain that towers over the city. It is an enigmatic device, celebrating the landscape that defines Cape Town. It is also a gentle satire on the reverence that people have for Table Mountain.

As a structure it is more permanent than fireworks and more movable than the Eiffel Tower. *Halo* has the potential to be used as an instrument of cultural diplomacy: it could be suspended over the Giardini in Venice, the Maracanã Football Stadium in Rio, or even the United Nations headquarters in New York. The structure of the halo—based on the concept of tensegrity developed by Buckminster Fuller in the 1950s—can be supported in various ways to allow adaptation in many different sites.

The celestial light quality of *Halo* can radically transform locations and ignite new uses of public space. Even when removed, *Halo* leaves an afterimage in which its absence is as memorable as its presence. The capacity for satire gives this divine ring some teeth; it can be a critical presence.

*Project Team*
Heinrich Wolff, Ilze Wolff, Maria Wolff, Lawden Holmes, Bayo Windapo, Chris Mulder, Stefan van Biljon, Oguzhan Sivrikaya, Ant Vervoort

*Acknowledgements*
Interactive Africa, LH Consulting Engineers, James Puttick

# WORKAC + ANT FARM
## *San Francisco / New York City, US*
## 3-C.CITY: Climate, Convention, and Cruise

Image: C.City section, WORKac

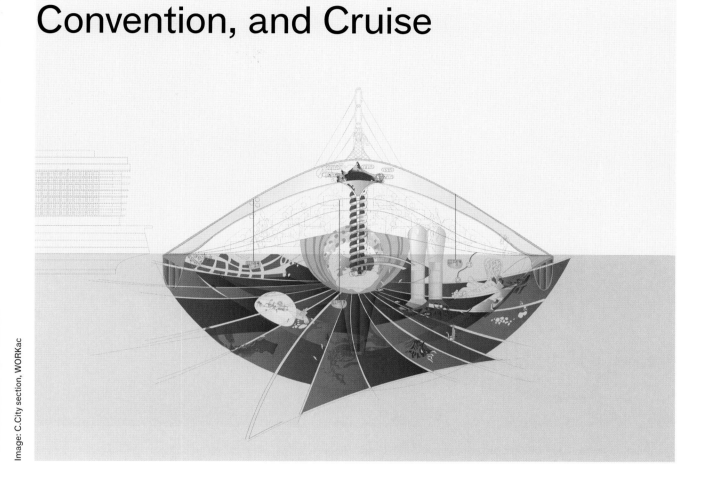

*3-C.CITY: Climate, Convention, and Cruise*, a collaboration between Ant Farm and WORKac, reexamines three of Ant Farm's seminal projects, the House of the Century, Convention City, and Dolphin Embassy, which date from between 1972 and 1976.

It began with a conversation between WORKac and Ant Farm, which led to the creation of a series of drawings and diagrams of the three projects—imagining previously undrawn floor plans or sections, and submitting them to intense analysis. This gave rise to a new project that nests, weaves, scales, and displaces themes from the original works into the contemporary context.

*3-C.CITY* transforms Ant Farm's polemical explorations of a counter-America for our present post-American time, one in which climate change, rising sea levels, and sinking cities all tell us that we need to engage in urgent diplomacy among all the species living with us.

The project translates into a set of issues, or critical overlaps, that guides both practices: Art and Architecture, Politics, Communication, Form, Scale, Environment, Systems, Food,

Diplomacy, The Future, and Counter- / Post-America. These questions open up possibilites for alternative practices that have evolved over the past forty years.

The state of the art of architecture is not one frozen point in time, but a continuous dialogue. Architecture is a relational practice, one that is constantly remade by questioning its own dogmas, expanding its canon, negating its center, inhabiting the edges, and rewriting its histories.

*3-C.CITY* is a city on the sea with a synthetic harbor, where docking is welcome. It is a vessel and a vehicle of dreams. It is a center for discussing and negotiating worldwide issues, for hard-science research and for social issues. It is a learning environment and an active agent of change.

*Project Team*
Amale Andraos, Dan Wood, Chip Lord, Curtis Schreier, Chije Kang, Tom Goddeeris, Madeeha Merchant, Jun Deng, Laetitia Fontenat, Margaux Guillot

# YASMEEN LARI + HERITAGE FOUNDATION OF PAKISTAN
## *Karachi, Pakistan*
## Barefoot Architecture

Architect Yasmeen Lari and her husband, historian Suhail Zaheer Lari, cofounded the Heritage Foundation of Pakistan in 1980 with the aim of protecting the country's built heritage. Following a massive earthquake in Pakistan in 2005, her attention turned to post-disaster recovery. Lari developed a sustainable design strategy based on the pursuit of low carbon emissions, disaster risk resilience, and disaster preparedness, and on fostering pride in vernacular heritage and local traditions. The construction techniques she proposes enable disenfranchised communities to become self-reliant by dealing with physical and social deficits themselves.

The construction of 40,000 of Lari's KaravanShelters, built with mud, lime, and bamboo in over 1,700 villages in partnership with the International Organization for Migration, has placed Pakistan in the lead of zero-carbon self-built shelter programs. In addition, over 15,000 self-built Rural Designer Chulha-Kitchens—fuel-efficient smokeless stoves placed on earthen platforms—have been constructed and decorated by village women. Similarly, hundreds of self-built eco-toilets are preventing open defecation in the countryside, enabling households, and especially women, to achieve a more dignified existence and a healthier environment.

The innovative use of locally sourced clay, low-energy lime, and renewable bamboo provides low-cost seismic- and flood-resistant alternatives for construction in disaster-prone areas. The training programs for green skills developed under Lari's guidance provide women with technical competence, enabling them to mitigate the prevalent culture of dependency.

Over one hundred women have been selected over the course of many village meetings, and have become experts in the execution of such construction procedures. In order to generate income, they have begun to market products such as eco-toilets, fuel-efficient stoves, and organic compost, thus helping to regenerate the local economy.

Lari's *Barefoot Architecture* has been designed for low-income countries, with the aim of improving the conditions of disaster-affected households suffering from core poverty. Yet the adoption of similar systems in richer countries—where construction materials require high amounts of energy and water, thus significantly contributing to global warming—could prove equally valuable.

*Project Team*
Yasmeen Lari, Naheem Shah

Bold: Alternative Scenarios for Chicago
Organized by Iker Gil

*Bold: Alternative Scenarios for Chicago* presents eighteen projects and ideas for the city of Chicago. They are generated by both emerging and established local architects and designers who are rethinking the future of the city without the need to respond to a brief by a client. In that sense, the exhibition explores alternative scenarios for the city as well as the agency of the architect in shaping them. While they were conceived without a client, the projects take into account the constraints and realities of Chicago and aim to engage in fruitful conversations with public and private agencies to shape the city's future.

The exhibition offers alternative strategies to key issues at stake in Chicago, at multiple scales: regional studies exploring interconnected layers (such as biodiversity dynamics, agricultural production, and hydrology) that have emerged as pressing topics in the Chicago region over the past decade; urban strategies addressing ecological and infrastructural challenges, while providing a sustainable revenue stream and conceptualizing new civic possibilities; speculative proposals investigating the urban design potential of Chicago's vacant lots; innovative high-rise typologies that marry the latest technology, economic considerations, and idealized urban domestic life; new forms of architecture (aesthetic, spatial, and social) that embrace technology's influence on human sensory perception and environmental control; and a reexamination of issues, such as the use of history in the design of architecture and contemporary ideas surrounding libraries and the city, sparked by a late entry to the 1987 Harold Washington Library Center competition.

The same issues are also being explored by disciplines other than architecture; different lenses complement, expand, and even question our understanding of the city from an architectural perspective. The exhibition encourages such exchange through the inclusion of two projects that use mapping and photography as their primary ways of looking at the state of the city. These projects document our relationship with vacancy, questioning how we might bridge disparate experiences, and what the relationship between planning and informality is, as well as uncovering the stories hidden in the city through the abstraction and isolation of big data.

The eighteen projects in the show, along with a series of related events, are an opportunity to debate the issues Chicago is facing, the possibilities they present, and the challenges to be overcome. Each of them has the potential to foster a long-lasting conversation about the possible futures of Chicago.

# DAVID BROWN
## The Available City

*The Available City* is an ongoing exploration of Chicago's ownership of 15,000 vacant city lots as an opportunity to impact the smallest increment of the city grid—the individual lot. Rather than presenting 15,000 separate projects that lack clarity about their urban effects, *The Available City* proposes a publicly accessible collective space system in which each city-owned lot has potential as a surface element in that system, as a softscape, hardscape, or small building by a local nonprofit organization or the city. Lots that are adjacent to privately owned vacant lots have additional potential to provide volumes of collective space within buildings on two to five lots.

In this proposal, buildings that incorporate city-owned lots receive increased footprint and square footage allowances through the provision of publicly accessible collective space with a collective surface area that is at least equal to the area of the city lots. Higher building heights are attainable by meeting the requirements of collective space volume with a surface area exceeding the area of the lots used. *The Available City* is thus an urban proposition comprised of 15,000 local effects in which the provision of greater amounts of collective space is the basis for increased amounts of building.

Designed to be flexible, nonhierarchical, incremental, open-ended, and variable in its outcome, the proposition gains in impact as each collective space, independently complete and viable, increases and intertwines with others.

*The Available City* is not an a priori plan, but an introduction of new qualities and relationships. Through a set of rules regarding building mass, and dimensions of collective space, the proposition actualizes the map of city-owned vacant lots in a way that leverages existing differences in vacant land ownership in order to introduce a new form of public space. While farms and forests—the current popular considerations for unoccupied urban land—are two latent modalities embedded within the project, the emphasis is on culture rather than cultivation. Developed exclusively as surfaces, the proposition provides a collective spatial system equal in size to Chicago's Loop.

It is anticipated that the collective space is itself a variable, an incentive and attractor, impacting the actual outcome. Through the accumulation of distinct instances, the forms and activities become varied enough for a range of individuals to connect. *The Available City* solicits wide participation in the speculation of what this new space, and consequently the neighborhoods in which the city-owned lots are prevalent, could be.

*Project Team*
Cady Chintis, Matthew Van Der Ploeg, Christina Stamatoukos (research); Jared Macken, Lyndsay Pepple (general design proposition and design development); George Louras, Jared Macken, Cole Monaghan, Ji Noh, Tafhim Rahman, Matthew Schneider, Jenna Wolf (design development); Jacob Comerci, Nicholas Krause, George Louras, Cole Monaghan, Roy Mwale, Lyndsay Pepple, Mark Rowntree, Julia Sedlock, Jenna Wolff (2012 Architecture Venice Biennale); DeptUS/ Adrianne Joergensen, Jason Mould (scapes and chambers); Matthew Schneider (Switch-A-Shape 2D): David Ramis (3D)

*Acknowledgements*
Graham Foundation

1. 3D DESIGN STUDIO
Making Architecture that Heals
*Project Team*
A. Melinda Palmore,
Darryl G. Crosby

2. ANIA JAWORSKA
Forum Pavilion

3. CENTRAL STANDARD
OFFICE OF DESIGN
Cut/Fill
*Project Team*
Alejandra Edery-Ferre,
Ruta Misiunas; Chen-Han Tu,
Lukasz Wojnicz

1

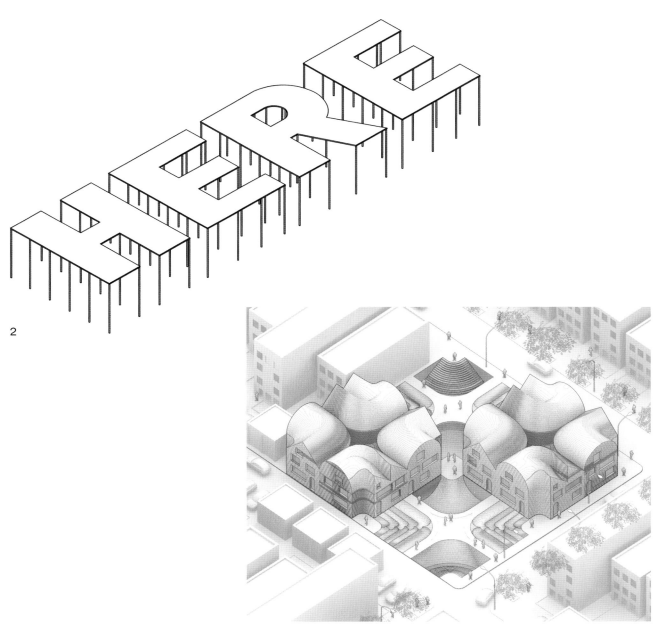

2

3

4. JAHN
KTC234: Knowledge Trade Center
*Project Team*
Francisco Gonzalez-Pulido; Jonathan Gately,
Phil Stott;  Werner Sobek; Joe Madon, Maria Miller

5. JGMA
Reimagining Wellness
in Humboldt Park

6. KRUECK + SEXTON
Chicago Boogie-Woogie
*Project Team*
Tom Jacobs, Mircea Eni, Sean Myung Shin Kim,
Elias Logan, Don Semple, Lindsey Telford

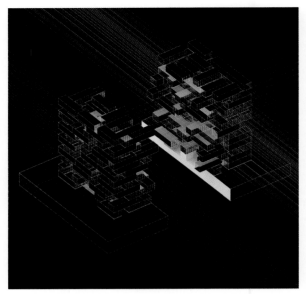

4

5

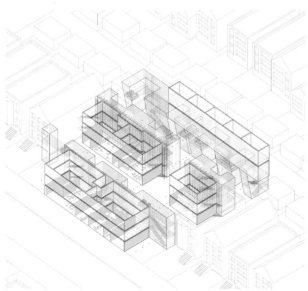

6

**7. MARGARET MCCURRY**
Circle the Wagons
*Project Team*
Margaret McCurry, Margaret Sullivan

**8. LANDON BONE BAKER**
Small Industries in South Chicago

**9. STANLEY TIGERMAN**
Cluster Container Housing for the Disabled
*Project Team*
Stanley Tigerman, Jessie LaFree

7

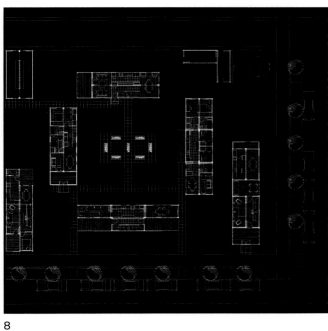

8

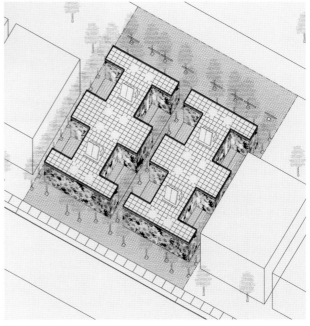

9

# DAVID SCHALLIOL
# Reckoning with Vacancy

In Chicago, the place where one lives affects how one understands vacancy. In many North Side neighborhoods and Near Northwest Side areas, vacancy heralds the construction of larger and more expensive buildings, while in many South and West Side neighborhoods, vacancy is the harbinger of yet another derelict lot. The result is that while many Chicago neighborhoods are maintaining—if not gaining—density, other sections of the city are increasingly sparse.

*Reckoning with Vacancy* grapples with these divergent conditions by concentrating on the city's South and West Sides, where the last several decades have brought major changes to the built environment and the communities that inhabit it. From coordinated efforts like the Chicago Housing Authority's Plan for Transformation to the more chaotic effect of the Great Recession's foreclosure crisis, these events have dramatically affected the neighborhoods many of us call home.

While some vacant properties are targeted for long-term development or are absorbed in the city's vacant property ownership programs, the majority of these parcels are in an ambiguous position: either informally maintained by community members or derelict and seemingly up for grabs. How are we to understand such sites, and how can residents and municipal planners work with them? This orientation also allows us to engage with broader puzzles related to the city's future, including which factors determine vacancy, how we might bridge disparate experiences of vacancy, and how we might understand the relationship between planning and informality.

100

# DESIGN WITH COMPANY
## Late Entry to the Chicago Public Library Competition

This *Late Entry to the Chicago Public Library Competition* uses the parameters of the 1987 architectural competition as a framework to reexamine the issues at stake not only in the original design brief but also in the choice of the winning scheme, the use of history in the design of architecture, and contemporary ideas surrounding libraries and the city. The "late entry" format borrows from Claes Oldenburg's *Late Entry to the Chicago Tribune Tower Competition* as well as Stanley Tigerman's exhibition of the same name from 1980. With this reboot, Design With Company is drawing a connection between the Tribune Tower and the Public Library competitions, both of which have been instrumental in shaping attitudes toward architecture in Chicago. Both competitions resulted in buildings that self-consciously deploy historical forms and ornament to communicate with the public.

Certain architects and writers have been critical of these outcomes, with Tigerman quoted as saying, "By selecting that scheme [for the Chicago Public Library], it sends Chicago backwards, away from its own future precisely the way the Tribune Competition and the Columbian Exposition did. Because it is a building that's a study in dissimilation that feigns to be something of a time that is not ours, that uses as a role model the Bibliothèque Sainte-Geneviève in Paris by Henri Labrouste. That's the problem with the kind of thinking that uses context to establish authority and uses verification of an earlier time to get over the insecurities of the natives of a city trying to seek authenticity."

This project contends explicitly with Tigerman's misgivings about the use of history in architectural design, not necessarily to correct or solve the problem but to revisit the polemic in a revealing and contemporary way.

*Project Team*
Stewart Hicks, Allison Newmeyer, Jeisler Salunga, France La, Obed Lopez, Andrew Newmeyer

# HINTERLANDS URBANISM AND LANDSCAPE
## Logistical Ecologies

Image: Chris Bennett, 2014

*Logistical Ecologies* proposes the urbanization of northeastern Illinois according to planetary logistics networks and regional ecologies, with an emphasis on biodiversity, agriculture, and hydrology. The strategy co-locates housing, retail, warehousing, distribution facilities, and intermodal freight facilities according to dynamic environmental processes, regional land uses, and transportation infrastructure.

Since the deregulation of the transportation industry in the 1980s, the use of the shipping container for transporting goods manufactured in newly industrializing Asian countries to sites of consumption in the United States has given rise to vast logistical landscapes. This backstage network of rails, warehousing, and distribution facilities sustains the front-stage lifestyles commonly associated with the so-called city. Despite this inseparable link, in North America design disciplines all too often focus on dense central business districts or waterfront brownfields as sites for intervention.

*Logistical Ecologies* uses new analytical categories rooted in the fields of ecology, landscape architecture, transportation geography, and critical urban theory to uncover new methods and sites of intervention. By doing so, the project produces a more holistic reading of twenty-first-century urbanization than many of the existing theoretical frameworks and analytical categories allow.

Within the broader framework of logistics and ecology, three lines of inquiry form the foundation for a new urbanization strategy for northeastern Illinois:

1. Biodiversity dynamics: As land uses continue to shift regionally, mega-faunal species such as coyotes, bison, and bobcats are establishing new ranges and adapting to the dynamics of twenty-first century-urbanization. How can these be integrated into an urbanization strategy?

2. Agricultural production: Logistics nodes like intermodal freight facilities and logistics networks like double-stack corridors are often at odds with farmers and their highly productive agricultural land in northeastern Illinois. How can a more nuanced reading of soils, land uses, and existing infrastructure help resolve this tension?

3. Hydrology: A combination of unpredictable weather events and low permeability levels across the region are leading to major flooding events in areas like the Fox River Valley. How can an urbanization strategy work with, rather than against, these dynamics?

*Project Team*
Conor O'Shea (founder and principal), Chris Bennett (architectural collaborator), Luke Hegeman (MODUS Collective)

*Acknowledgements*
Aneesha Dharwadker

# MICHAEL PECIRNO
# Of All of the Facts
# and All of the Figures

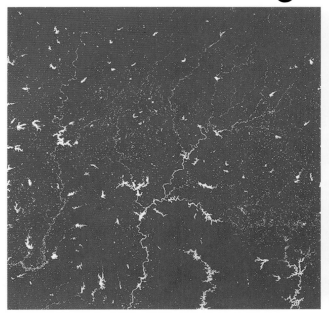 

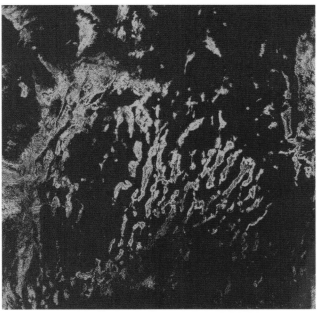

Over the past few years, cities have rushed to establish data stores and data portals, places in which anyone with Internet access can log on, download a data set, and often visualize it directly in the browser. This data can be anything that fits neatly into a spreadsheet, and its topic can range from the locations of police stations to lists of "problem landlords." But aside from an act of novelty or visualization, can these spreadsheets change the way we perceive our cities, or are they just a trend fueled by buzzwords like "big data"?

*Of All of the Facts and All of the Figures* takes a dive into Chicago's Data Portal to find out what spreadsheets can tell us about our city. What can happen when we begin to isolate individual features and separate them from the ubiquitous background of the political map? Through the abstraction and isolation of big data, we find that the city begins to tell a story too often obscured by geography, boundaries, and our own history.

103

# PORT URBANISM
## The Big Shift

*The Big Shift* explores Chicago's relationship to its lakefront by challenging the common perception of it as a fixed, unalterable line defining the edge of the city. Although popularly considered "forever open, clear, and free," in reality, Chicago's lakefront has been in a constant state of transformation over the last 150 years. The result is the creation of more than 1,000 acres of new land and the construction of dozens of buildings, all of which continue to be dominated by the changing configurations of Lake Shore Drive. Much of this transformation has been economically and politically motivated throughout the city's shifting economy. The proposed project has two parts that call attention to this hidden reality.

Part One — *The Big Shift* Exhibition
*The Big Shift* imagines a scenario where Chicago embraces the lakefront's latent potential with a dramatic, yet conceptually simple infrastructural transformation. By shifting the 1.5 mile stretch of Lake Shore Drive running eastward along Grant Park, the city could create upwards of 225 acres of new lakefront real estate — importantly, west of Lake Shore Drive. This would generate an enormous, long-term revenue stream in land leases and property taxes, despite the significant upfront costs. The *Shift* would allow for the reconfiguration of Lake Shore Drive to reduce its adverse impact on pedestrian and bike access to the lakefront, as well as its auditory and emission impacts on the city.

More significantly, the project enhances two of Chicago's most beloved public spaces: a fourth street wall frames the east side of Grant Park, creating a "Central Park" condition. Stately, tree-lined boulevards connect from the west side of Grant Park across Lake Shore Drive to a new 145 acre public waterfront.

This new waterfront includes softly rolling topography, beaches, spaces of prospect and refuge, as well as generous planting, pedestrian circulation, and street furniture. The proposal more than triples the size of the current lakefront adjacent to Grant Park, providing the recreational amenities now missing from the area.

Simply put, *The Big Shift* imagines a scenario where a public infrastructural renovation creates urgently needed municipal revenue sources while enhancing and expanding Chicago's most important public spaces and civic assets.

Part Two — *Marking the Edge* Installation
A companion to *The Big Shift* exhibition, *Marking the Edge* catalyzes the public imagination of the lakefront by marking the lake's edge within the city at three points in time: the past, approximately 1870, the period just before the Great Fire; the present, the lakefront edge in 2015; and the future circa 2040, a speculative lakefront that includes moving Lake Shore Drive eastward and the development of a third street wall for Grant Park.

These three lines will be temporarily inscribed on the city in a playful, graphic, highly legible way that invites the public to consider their relationship to the ever-changing lakefront. The markings include embedded information related to each respective edge and will be centered on the Chicago Cultural Center, Grant Park, and Monroe Harbor.

*Project Team*
Andrew Moddrell, Christopher Marcinkoski,
Brandon Biederman, Selina Chiu, Alexander Culler,
Ryan Hernandez, Laura-Anne Wong, Chi Yin Lee

*Acknowledgements*
Marcia Lausen, Tim Wilson (Studio/lab); Michelle Ha-Tucker,
IDEO

# SOM + CAMESGIBSON
## The High Life

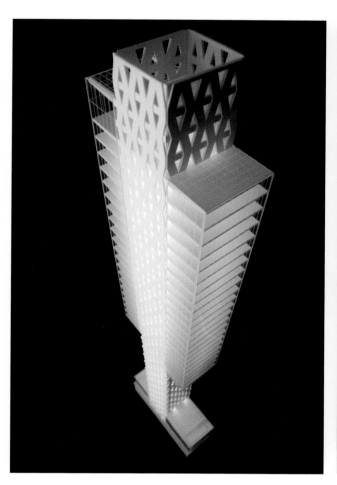

No product has been a better quantifier of modernity's value for architecture than the high-rise building. With a history fueled in equal parts by technological innovation and economic motivation, the typology of the high-rise evolved from its early phase as a vertical extrusion of property limits and a generic frame holding an undefined program into a varied group of building types with distinct subcategories. While the office tower may offer the richest history of the typology's past—especially in Chicago—the residential high-rise building is its future.

As the world's population continues to urbanize, new forms of the residential high-rise building will be required to improve urban life. Dense stacks of formulaic dwelling units that house some of the global population's wealthiest and poorest inhabitants have left little room for the varied (and economically mobile) middle class, which in turn hinders any dense neighborhood's capacity to grow or sustain social and economic diversity. The history and current (highly segregated) state of Chicago could not provide a better example of this point. In suggesting an alternative model from what has been historically attempted or is currently offered in Chicago, *The High Life* reorders technology, economic motivations, and idealized urban domestic life to aid in the city's ongoing evolution into a more resilient community, while continuing Chicago's long history of developing innovative tall buildings.

*Project Team*
Brian Lee, Bill Baker, Andrew Obendorf, Benton Johnson, Arathi Gouda, Maged Guerguis, Mark Nagis, Justin Peterson, Jacob Gay, Greg Derrico (SOM); Grant Gibson, Aura Venckunaite, Drew Stanley (CAMESgibson)

# URBANLAB
# Filter Island

In the 1909 *Plan of Chicago*, Daniel Burnham sought to harmonize two physical systems that had always been incompatible along Chicago's lakefront: transportation and recreation. Reenvisioned transportation networks included realigned railroads, new roadways, and new harbors. Burnham also envisioned a continuous recreational park on the lakefront, filled with new public buildings and amenities that synthesized technical necessities with cultural enhancements.

A decade before Burnham's *Plan*, engineers directed the flow of the Chicago river from Lake Michigan to the Mississippi River via canals, transforming the river into a model of water management and transportation infrastructure. At the time, this was critical for the health and prosperity of Chicagoans.

Today, the city faces new challenges. Massive rainstorms often cause raw sewage overflow into Lake Michigan. Additionally, the river has become a two-way conduit for invasive species, causing damage to water infrastructures and ecosystems from Lake Michigan to the Gulf of Mexico.

*Filter Island* seeks to redesign the river and conceptualize new civic possibilities, drawing from Chicago's legacy of leveraging infrastructural improvements for new civic space. The first step toward this dual goal is to dam the Chicago River near the confluence of its three branches: the North Branch, the South Branch, and the Chicago River. By damming the river, three branches transform into two separate waterways: the new South Branch and the new Chicago River. The new Chicago River would flow between two mouths of Lake Michigan: the southern mouth in downtown Chicago and the northern mouth in Wilmette, Illinois. The existing locks are removed between river and lake resulting in the new Chicago River becoming an extension of the lake.

Damming the river will halt the transmission of invasive species and prevent yearly losses of Lake Michigan water currently leaking through the existing locks. But because the river will continue to flow sewage into the lake during rainstorms, a new approach is needed to remove dangerous toxins and microbes.

*Filter Island* cleans the new Chicago River by filtering pollutants in a series of large-scale bio-cells. Polluted water flows into *Filter Island* over a shallow waterfall at the northern edge of the island. Through a series of wetlands and bio-pools, polluted water is cleaned of contaminants before being discharged into the lake. The ratio of water-cleansing landscape to park program landscape flips as the park extends southward. The whole island is wrapped in a programmed edge that includes beaches, pathways, and breakwaters. A new dry-dock transfer exchange along the eastern extension of the new Chicago River will accommodate boat traffic between the river and lake.

Rather than hide the water-cleaning process, *Filter Island* reveals it. Rather than employing a heavy, industrial, energy-intensive system, it is a passive, low-energy water-treatment sponge. Most importantly, *Filter Island* is a hybrid landscape combining the transportation of water with new recreational spaces.

*Project Team*
Sarah Dunn, Martin Felsen. Jeffrey Macias, Matthew Busscher, Matthew Schneider, Aishwarya Keshav, Anya Nair, Austin Tsai, Michelangelo La Tona

*Acknowledgements*
Illinois Institute of Technology, University of Illinois at Chicago, Chicago Architecture Foundation

106

# WEATHERS with AECOM
# Second Sun

Two of the greatest pressures on society today include humanity's manipulation of the environment and the advancement of bioengineering for the human body. The first changes the makeup of physical space; the second, the very body that perceives that space. At this intersection are the physical boundaries that define architectural space. The focus of *Second Sun* is to integrate these two rapidly advancing industries as an epicenter of architecture's spatial, social, environmental, and ethical discourse.

The public parks of global cities are the backbone of leisure, recreation, health, and community engagement. Yet as the energy crisis and global warming continue, and as billions of dollars are invested in wearable technologies, parks are increasingly passive spaces subject to climate and weather.

Instead, technologies that manipulate the environment have shown that outdoor public space can be designed and organized through energy (for instance, street lighting creates an area of light, transforming the way outdoor space can be used). History will point to the advent of street lighting as an early example of an architecture that grew more robust and layered with additional energy systems. The architectural space of street lighting is the product of energy that has been tuned to the sensory perception of the human body. This innovation changed the fundamental underpinnings of leisure, recreation, safety, and community engagement in our cities.

As wearable technologies enhance our body's perception, thermal, acoustic, electromagnetic, and chemical energy will take the role of new building materials, giving rise to new spatial typologies and aesthetics.

*Project Team*
Sean Lally, Marina Nicollier, Veronica Gomez, Angela Ngo, Maged Guerguis

LAKE

KIOSK

In partnership with the Chicago Park District and the City of Chicago, the Chicago Architecture Biennial commissioned the design and construction of four new kiosks for the shoreline of Lake Michigan, a celebrated and heavily used public space that is a major destination for both visitors and local residents.

One of the projects has been chosen through an open international competition that took place in the spring of 2015, chaired by architects David Adjaye and Sharon Johnston, artistic directors Joseph Grima and Sarah Herda, Michael J. O'Brien (BP), and Rob Rejman (Chicago Park District). The winning team received the BP Prize, which included a $10,000 honorarium and a $75,000 budget to realize the design. BP is the presenting sponsor of the Chicago Architecture Biennial, and has a longstanding commitment to supporting architecture in Chicago. The competition attracted 420 entries from more than forty countries around the world.

The other three kiosks have been designed in a collaboration between local architecture schools and three internationally renowned architectural firms.

The four kiosks are on display in various locations around the city for the duration of the Biennial, before being installed, in the spring of 2016, on the lakefront.

FRONTS

# ULTRAMODERNE
## Chicago Horizon
### *Winner of BP Prize*

*Chicago Horizon* seeks to build the largest flat wooden roof possible with the available budget. Using cross-laminated timber (a carbon-negative engineered lumber product) in the largest dimensions commercially available, the kiosk aims to provide an excess of public space for Chicago beach-goers.

The generous 56 ft. (17 m) square offers an architectural lending library and a shelter from the elements during its time in Millennium Park. It will later become a large shading canopy overlooking Lake Michigan, with space for commercial vendors. *Chicago Horizon* expresses the concepts of lightness at a variety of scales, from the 8 ft. (2.5 m) hovering roof plane to the viewing platform and vending kiosk, which are suspended from the roof using chain-link fencing without any additional supports.

The horizontal reach of the roof recalibrates the experience of two extremes of the Chicago landscape: at ground level, the Lake Michigan horizon dominates, forming a line of symmetry between ground and canopy. From the viewing platform, the roof becomes a new artificial horizon, shutting out the foreground and emphasizing the vertical Chicago skyline above an abstract floating plane.

*Project Team*
Yasmin Vobis, Aaron Forrest, Brett Schneider

*Current Kiosk Site*
Museum Campus
Northwest of Shedd Aquarium at the lakefront

# INDEPENDENT ARCHITECTURE & PAUL PREISSNER ARCHITECTS + UIC SCHOOL OF ARCHITECTURE
## Summer Vault

*Summer Vault* is a lakefront kiosk that accommodates a variety of cultural activities. It consists of basic geometric shapes—a 12 ft. (4 m) diameter barrel vault, a parallelogram, some triangles—which combine to create a peculiar, freestanding hangout within Millennium Park and the Lakefront.

The interior of the skewed vault is divided into two triangular spaces—one enclosed by expanded metal screens and doors, and one open to the air but still within the vaulting. This two-part floor plan allows for commerce and gatherings to occur simultaneously. It also reflects the origins of the kiosk typology—garden pavilions in thirteenth-century Persia—while enabling its contemporary use as a seasonal commercial space and festive park retreat.

*Project Team*
Paul Andersen, Kevin Hirth, Jason King, Paul Preissner (architects); Siobhan Barrett, Matthew Busscher, Jesus Corral (UIC School of Architecture); Goodfriend Magruder Structure (structural engineering); Chicago Metal Rolled Products (steel supplier); K&K Iron Works (vault fabrication); Cramblit's Welding (doors and screen fabrication); Schneider Surfboards (furniture)

*Current Kiosk Site*
Chase Promenade, Millennium Park

# NLÉ + SCHOOL OF THE ART INSTITUTE OF CHICAGO
## Rock

*ROCK* is a pop-up pavilion, sculpturally composed from the raw and historic limestone blocks that once protected the city's shoreline. Its bold yet delicate balance aims to transform Chicago's lakefront into a magnet for social and cultural life.

Located at Montrose Beach on the Lake Michigan shoreline, the kiosk is conceived as an "infrastructural box" consisting of materials and technology that are found in or belong to the environment. The structural system uses limestone and concrete elements that can be assembled in multiple configurations to suit different locations and uses along the lakefront—providing shelter and accommodating different vendors, while contributing to the protection of the shoreline.

*Project Team*
Kunlé Adeyemi, Marco Cestarolli, Karien Hofhuis, Bethan Nelson, Berend Strijland (NLÉ); Douglas Pancoast, Kat elyn Barbaria,Tanner Jackson Bowman, Ik Hun Chang, Yinjie Deng, Chaim Emanuel, Hyun Sik Kim, Nayoung Lim, Yeonji Park, Kelly Grace Sullivan, Zaiyuan Xiao, Yunzhuo Hao (SAIC); Ken Maschke, Nate Sosin, Lizabeth DuBay (Thornton Tomasetti)

*With the support of*
Pepper Construction; Theaster Gates

*Current Kiosk Site*
Chase Promenade, Millennium Park

112

# PEZO VON ELLRICHSHAUSEN + IIT COLLEGE OF ARCHITECTURE
## Cent Pavilion

The slender and stable figure is meant to convey a sense of silent and convoluted simplicity. It is self-centered, self-regulated, and self-located as an opaque monolith without any scale, direction, or hierarchy, as a podium for an invisible statue. The silhouette seems fairly redundant—an attenuated transition from wall to roof—for a single, oversized room. Its construction has a simple structural logic. It is unwisely rational, since the same corner detail is repeated all over and the same diagonal bracing underpins every center. But the handcrafted elements should imply delight over thought.

This kiosk is a device that embodies a multiplicity of visual references: from Hockney's inverted perspectives, Morandi's *natura morta*, or Guarini's telescopic domes to anonymous bell towers, water towers, lighthouses, silos, or chimneys—or even an inaccessible, metaphorical purgatory for the next high-rise building.

*Project Team*
Mauricio Pezo, Sofia von Ellrichshausen; Paul Endres (structure); Richard Nelson (construction)

*Current Kiosk Site*
Illinois Institute of Technology

113

STONY ISLA A

A new exhibition venue on the South Side of Chicago, Stony Island Arts Bank aims to be both an international platform for contemporary art and a cultural space for the local community. The building was formerly a bank, built in 1923, closed in the 1980s, and abandoned since then. Its refurbishment and programming have been initiated by the Rebuild Foundation under the direction of artist Theaster Gates. The public opening of Stony Island Arts Bank and its inaugural exhibition are taking place as part of the Chicago Architecture Biennial.

# CARLOS BUNGA
## *Barcelona, Spain*
## Under the Skin

Following a one-month residency at the Stony Island Arts Bank, Carlos Bunga has created a large-scale installation titled Under the Skin. This is the inaugural exhibition at the Bank, a new venue founded by artist Theaster Gates. In his work, Bunga creates in situ installations that refer to and intervene in their immediate surroundings. Under the Skin responds to the existing architecture and ongoing restoration of the Bank. Made out of cardboard and painted white, the ephemeral installation occupies the Bank's central hall; viewers are prompted to enter and engage with the monumental yet temporary structure, which inhabits a rehabilitated architectural space.

Evoking the interior of a basilica, Under the Skin tests the verticality of the Bank, appropriating elements of the preexisting architecture: its flooring, ceiling, and columns. The installation blurs the symbolism implicit in both typologies—a church and a bank—as well as the boundaries between architecture, sculpture, and painting.

In a time when society is dominated by a market culture, Bunga offers a space of silence, inviting us to reflect on the passage of time, on the relationships between existing power structures, and on the fragility of architecture itself.

# FRIDA ESCOBEDO
*Mexico City, Mexico*
## Material Reservoir

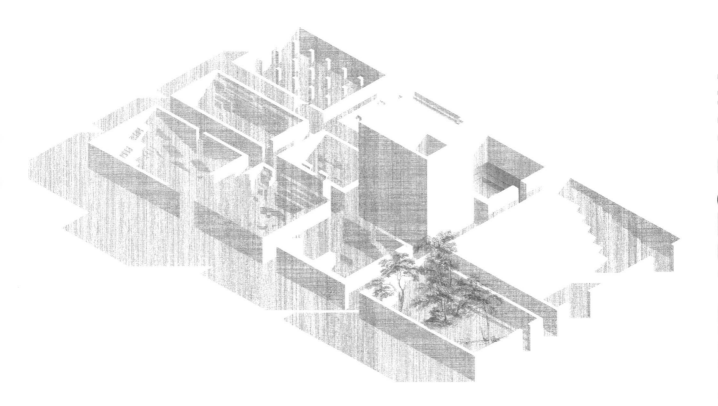

Parts, piled, piles, broken, pieces, stacks, clastic, stacked, identical, interchangeable—minimalist sculptor Carl Andre carefully selected these words as a preface to his own work, words that can also be used to describe Frida Escobedo's *Material Reservoir*. The project creates a series of spaces to complement Theaster Gates's Stony Island Art Bank, a platform for site-specific commissions and exhibitions, a venue for artist and scholar residencies, and a home for the Rebuild Foundation's archives and collections. In the area, a number of abandoned and dilapidated buildings are being bulldozed by the city of Chicago to address the problem of violence in its South Side neighborhood. This conflict unfolds in space: appropriation is confused with domination. The exchange value of space overshadows its use value. As a consequence, the streets are peppered with vacant lots with heaps of terracotta bricks—an iconic element of Chicago's architectural tradition is disregarded as rubble.

The demolition debris is used to create a series of thick-walled courtyards. The bricks are stacked simply so that the walls can be deconstructed and reconstructed in a number of different configurations. Bricks act as moving pieces on a game board, as tools for negotiation and consensus. The juxtaposition of this *Material Reservoir* with the empty vaults of the bank is symbolic. Each courtyard can be read as a reverse Tower of Babel, where communication, agency, and interaction will physically and symbolically demolish the wall to create a common ground to be repurposed or reappropriated by different actors. The weaving and unweaving of this shared landscape allows viewers to question and acknowledge the commonalities between matter and meaning.

*Project Team*
Frida Escobedo, Olivier Bellflamme, Natalia Gálvez, Federica Lombardi, Antonio Zarco; model by Rodolfo Díaz Cervantes (Taller Tornel)

WATER

GALLE

RI

The City Gallery, located in the historic Water Tower, is a familiar and treasured landmark located along the city's Magnificent Mile. Constructed between 1867 and 1869, the tower was created for Chicago's municipal water system, and originally housed a 135 ft. (40 m) iron standpipe used to regulate water pressure. It gained special significance as one of the few buildings to survive the destructive path of the Great Chicago Fire of 1871.

# ASSAF EVRON
## *Chicago, US*
## Athens and Oraibi

"It is the lesson from the old book: the kinship of Athens and Oraibi." These are the words art historian Aby Warburg used (rephrasing a line from *Faust*) to open his 1923 lecture on the Pueblo Indians. With the notion of kinship, Warburg meant that, when he travelled to Arizona at the end of the nineteenth century, he was at the same time in the Athens of more than 2000 years earlier. This simultaneity transcends mere imagination, and can be better described as a kind of synchronic being. The ornamented object, for Warburg, has the power to transport us along and across the history of human culture; a journey between pagan antiquity, Pueblo religion, and modernity.

*Athens and Oraibi* explores Warburg's concept of simultaneity through the contemporary architectural vernacular.

Warburg accompanied the lecture with his own photographs, illustrations, and notes, which presented the objects he found in the desert in an abstract language. His images of ancient Pueblo furnishings inspired Evron to think about everyday construction elements.

Home Depot mass-produced stair stringers are painted with a motif that echoes the visual language of Native American objects and of Greek pottery. At the same time, they resonate with early modernist art, such as Sonja Delaunay's textiles, and later American Minimalism. The photographs are mounted on various wallpapers of Middle Eastern desert landscapes.

120

WATER TOWER GALLERIES

# OFF-
# PROJE

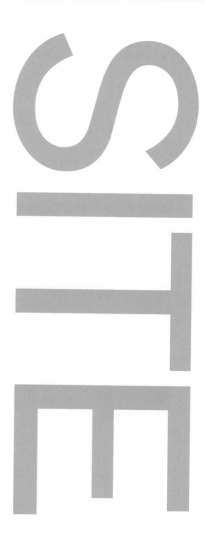

SITE

ECTS

# ANDRÉS JAQUE / OFFICE FOR POLITICAL INNOVATION
## *Madrid, Spain / New York City, US*
## Superpowers of Ten

In 1977, the Los Angeles office of Ray and Charles Eames produced *Powers of Ten: A Film Dealing with the Relative Size of Things in the Universe and the Effect of Adding Another Zero*, which opens with a shot set on the lakefront of Chicago. This movie was the second cinematic adaptation that the Eameses made of the book *Cosmic View: The Universe in 40 Jumps*, which had been published in 1957 by the Dutch architect and educator Kees Boeke.

Both Boeke's book and the Eameses' movies were beautifully designed and produced as projects that were simultaneously architectural, political, and pedagogical. For decades, they were used as educational tools in schools all over Europe and the United States. They contributed to focusing the collective gaze into a linear progression, in which jumps in scale and the interaction between genes, bodies, societies, and technologies were seen as frictionless and apolitical.

With *Superpowers of Ten*, Andrés Jaque and the Office for Political Innovation reenact the Eameses' film in its original Chicago location. The large-scale performance recontextualizes the 1970s representation of complex systems into contemporary discourse.

*Superpowers of Ten* was developed and presented for the first time as part of New Publics, curated by José Esparza for "Close Closer," the 2013 Lisbon Architecture Triennial (directed by Beatrice Galilee).

*Project Team*
Paula Currás, Lubo Dragomirov, Roberto González García, Álvaro Guillén, Andrés Jaque, Irene Kargiou, William Mondejar; Jorge López Conde (sound artist, photographs); Roberto González García (set director)

*Guest Artists*
Álvaro Carrillo, Paula Currás, Eugenio Fernández, Rebeca Hourdaki, Víctor Nouman, Ana Olmedo, Adrián Suárez, Enrique Ventosa

*Performance Details*
October 1–3, 2015
The Tank, Chicago Athletic Association

# SANTIAGO BORJA
## *Mexico City, Mexico*
## Theatre

The word "theater" refers not only to a place but also to an action; few words can do that. A place to watch, an action to play, a place to act upon; not surprisingly the same word also defines a place where conflict occurs and catharsis is found. *Theatre* is thus a project centered on the presence of the body as representation, on artificiality and cultural construction reworking the symbolic aspects of architecture—something that seems to be completely negated by most contemporary architectural practices.

*Theatre* is a disruptive reading of Mies van der Rohe's Carr Chapel, a brick-and-glass box for the Self and the transcendent. In this sense, the chapel embodies the conflict in modernism between pragmatism and belief. For Mies, a very simple structure devoid of any ornamentation—furnished with just a stainless steel cross and a silky curtain—would do. A curtain that is not merely a pure backdrop as in the Barcelona Pavilion but a lurking animated object that reminds us of the forces acting beyond our will. In Freudian terms, "the omnipotence of thought." Here, we can easily understand what Paul Rudolph meant when he said that in Mies's projects, "structure becomes symbolic."

In this context, *Theatre* is also about tracing diverse genealogies for modern architecture, from the primitive to the esoteric. Although this project makes reference to the history of architecture, it also reminds us of our anachronistic rapport with the sacred space, relinking spirituality with theatricality in a different guise.

But what interests us more is the reading of architecture as a place of re-creation, a place to perform. The concept of presence is fundamental to understanding the implications of *Theatre*: a stage and a performance at the same time; a site and the presentation of a real or imagined event. A stage is a transversal cut in the tissue of reality, splitting but also uniting the represented and the real. We should maybe ask then, is all architecture theater?

And then, what does it mean to be somewhere? A chapel is almost the embodiment of the interior space, a place where you contain and isolate yourself (*Innenraum*). It is not a place to roam; it is a place to be in. A space to abstract oneself from worldly contingencies, or to "find oneself," as Mies put it. That is why *Theatre* is also about spatial awareness—or spatial self-awareness, since there is always the I (*Raumbewusstsein*). An awareness that is both rational and irrational, where the juxtaposition of diverse belief systems defies the classical phenomenological or haptic readings of space perception. Paraphrasing Roland Barthes when defining "sitio," *Theatre* is just about finding the right place.

*Collaborators*
Grupo Palma Blanca, San Luis Atolotitlán; Grupo Capisayo, Santa María la Alta (Mexico); Eurythmeum CH, Dornach (Switzerland)

*Acknowledgements*
Mies van der Rohe Society, Chicago; Illinois Institute of Technology; CONACULTA-FONCA, Mexico; SRE-AMEXCID, Mexico

*Details*
Installation at the Robert F. Carr Memorial Chapel
Illinois Institute of Technology
Performances on October 1–2, 2015

# BRYONY ROBERTS +
# SOUTH SHORE DRILL TEAM
*Chicago, US*
We Know How to Order

We knew how to order. Just the dash
Necessary. ...
But nothing ever taught us to be islands.
And smart athletic language for this hour
Was not in the curriculum. No stout
Lesson showed how to chat with death. We brought
No brass fortissimo, among our talents,
To holler down the lions in the air.
—Gwendolyn Brooks

In a poem about African-American soldiers in World War II, Chicago poet Gwendolyn Brooks describes how military training filled soldiers with bold charisma but left them faltering in the lonely confrontation with death. Her poem captures the fragility of imposed order, as a defense against others and against death itself.

*We Know How to Order* is a reflection on systems of ordering the body and controlling the unknown in contemporary Chicago. Conceived by Bryony Roberts and choreographed by Asher Waldron, this site-specific performance brings young people from the South Side into a space of governmental and architectural authority.

Established in 1980 in the Chicago neighborhood of Greater Grand Crossing, the South Shore Drill Team is a source of entertainment and a way of bringing young people together to create a positive environment during their teenage years. Members of the South Shore Drill Team come from all areas of Chicago, and from very different backgrounds. They come together, in spite of such differences, to create precise performances that have toured around the United States.

The Federal Center, designed by Ludwig Mies van der Rohe and built between 1959 and 1974, is unified by an ever-present grid—a 4 ft. 8 in. (1.4 m) module that regulates the courthouse, post office, federal offices, and the plaza between them. When one stands in the plaza, the grid extends all around, from the paving stones underfoot to the bollards added after September 11, 2001. Multiple boundaries—from the surrounding office towers down to the bollards—keep the space devoid of urban activity.

*We Know How To Order* superimposes multiple ordering systems onto one another—street choreography onto precision drills onto the grid. Inverting the typical urban power dynamic, young people from the South Side take over this government-owned space, twisting its logic through their own movement.

This performance calls attention to the accessibility of public space in the US and to the way architecture, together with social expectations, influences the way people occupy common space; it also points to how we construct systems of order against the unknown, which, if pushed to a frenetic pitch, can produce exactly the uncertainty and release they were meant to contain.

The contrast of order and unpredictability in *We Know How to Order* correlates directly with the dualities in the lives of its young performers. Clean lines of movement are used and manipulated to create the unexpected. The choreography expands, contracts, and bends the grid of the Federal Center to connect the performance with the environment around it. The horizontal and vertical lines are reenacted by tossing batons and flags with the rise and fall of the music. The military style of drilling that has brought the South Shore Drill Team their fame accentuates the order and structure displayed by Mies van der Rohe's architecture. The performance of young people from the South Side in a downtown public space shows the possibility of new resonances between different spheres of the city.

*Project Team*
Bryony Roberts (artistic director); Asher Waldron (choreographer); South Shore Drill Team (performers); Arthur Robertson (executive director, SSDT)

*Performance Details*
October 2–3, 2015
Chicago Federal Center

GRAHAM

FOU

Founded in 1956, the Graham Foundation for Advanced Studies in the Fine Arts awards project-based grants to individuals and organizations and coordinates public programs to foster the development and exchange of diverse and challenging ideas about architecture and its role in the arts, culture, and society.

NDA
TION

# BARBARA KASTEN: STAGES

*October 1, 2015 – January 9, 2016*

Widely known for her photographs, artist Barbara Kasten has since the 1970s developed an expansive practice through the mediums of painting, textile, sculpture, theater, architecture, and installation. Organized in conversation with the artist and with access to her extensive archive, *Barbara Kasten: Stages* spans her five-decade engagement with abstraction, light, and architectural form, highlighting her critical engagement with architecture and her impact on a new generation of artists. The exhibition features Kasten's new site-specific video installation, which transforms the original ballroom of the Graham Foundation's historic Madlener House.

*Barbara Kasten: Stages* is organized by the Institute of Contemporary Art, University of Pennsylvania, and is curated by ICA curator Alex Klein.

*Acknowledgments*
Major support for *Barbara Kasten: Stages* has been provided by The Pew Center for Arts & Heritage, with additional support from the Nancy E. & Leonard M. Amoroso Exhibition Fund, Pamela Toub Berkman & David J. Berkman, Bortolami Gallery, the Carol T. & John G. Finley Fund, Kadel Willborn Gallery, the Marjorie E. & Michael J. Levine Fund, Toby Devan Lewis, Amanda & Andrew Megibow, Stephanie B. & David E. Simon, Babette L. & Harvey A. Snyder, and Meredith L. & Bryan S. Verona

Barbara Kasten installing the exhibition *Centric 2: Barbara Kasten, Installation/Photographs*, University Art Museum, California State University Long Beach, 1982. Courtesy of the artist and the University Art Museum

GRAHAM FOUNDATION

# PUBLIC PROGRAMS

The Chicago Architecture Biennial's public programs explore issues at the heart of the urban experience and the field of architecture. These events invite dialogue about how we construct, and conceive, the world in which we live.

*Late Night at the Biennial*
Fantastical performances, engaging experiences, and lively presentations by architects and artists enliven the Biennial on select Friday nights when the Cultural Center remains open until 9 pm. Visitors can enjoy open galleries and music.

*Architects on Film*
This weekly film series explores architecture through the lens of cinema. Local and visiting architects select a film that has touched their lives and careers. A conversation among panelists and the audience will follow the film. The series is presented in partnership with the Chicago International Film Festival.

*Pritzker Prize Laureate Lectures*
This lecture series highlights the work and ideas of previous winners of the Pritzker Prize, which is regarded as one of the highest honors in architecture.

*In Dialogue*
In Dialogue is a program of lectures where architects, scholars, and curators can discuss their ideas and practices and explore the meaning of architecture past and present.

*Tuesday Talks*
Architects, designers, curators, and scholars explore the state of the art of architecture and the future of the field through a series of lectures and panel discussions.

*The full program is available at chicagoarchitecturebiennial.org*

# PARTNER INSTITUTIONS
# AND EVENTS

# Art Institute of Chicago

The Art Institute of Chicago collects, preserves, and interprets works of art of the highest quality, representing the world's diverse artistic traditions for the inspiration and education of the public.

**Address**
111 S. Michigan Ave.
Chicago, IL 60603

**Contact**
312-443-3600
artic.edu

## MAKING PLACE: THE ARCHITECTURE OF DAVID ADJAYE
*September 19, 2015 – January 3, 2016*

With over fifty built projects across the world, David Adjaye is rapidly emerging as a major international figure in architecture and design. Rather than advancing a signature architectural style, Adjaye's structures address local concerns and conditions through both a historical understanding of context and a global understanding of modernism. The first comprehensive museum survey devoted to Adjaye, this exhibition offers an in-depth overview of the architect's distinctive approach and visual language with a dynamic installation design conceived by Adjaye Associates.

Of African ancestry and raised in Ghana, the Middle East, and England, Adjaye now has offices in London, New York, Berlin, and Accra. Like many contemporary architects, his practice defies cultural borders and geopolitical categories. However, Adjaye is unique in being an African-born architect working in a global landscape. Having traveled the world studying buildings and architectural styles, most recently

and extensively in Africa, he is acutely sensitive to the effects of location. A proponent for architecture from beyond the Western canon, he brings a distinctive contemporary "Afropolitan" view to his various projects.

## JEAN-LUC MYLAYNE: THE MILLENNIUM PARK CHAPEL
*May 22 – December 31, 2015*

French artist Jean-Luc Mylayne, acclaimed for his enigmatic color photographs of birds, has created a temporary chapel building with a 30 ft. (9 m) photo mural on its ceiling in Millennium Park, near the Lurie Garden East Walkway. In a hushed and darkened space, these brilliantly lit images show a sparrow, miraculously perched on the exact corner of a square roof, seemingly just over our heads. The pavilion accompanies a new exhibition of photographs by Mylayne at the Art Institute.

# Museum of Contemporary Art Chicago

The Museum of Contemporary Art Chicago offers exhibitions of the most thought-provoking art created since 1945. MCA Chicago documents contemporary visual culture through painting, sculpture, photography, video and film, and performance.

*Address*
220 E. Chicago Ave.
Chicago, IL 60611

*Contact*
12-280-2660
mcachicago.org

### MCA CHICAGO PLAZA PROJECT: ALEXANDRE DA CUNHA
*July 18, 2015 – July 24, 2016*

Brazilian artist Alexandre da Cunha is the fifth artist in the MCA's annual Summer Plaza project series. Da Cunha is known for finding creative ways of repurposing found objects—straw hats, plastic soda bottles, umbrellas. The MCA Plaza is enlivened by three of his interactive pieces, made from locally produced concrete sewer pipes and a concrete mixer. The materials have been displaced from their usual locations under Chicago's city streets or on the back of a cement truck and made accessible for visitors to step inside or peer into. The exhibit is curated by MCA chief curator Michael Darling.

### BMO HARRIS BANK CHICAGO WORKS: ANIA JAWORSKA
*August 25, 2015 – January 31, 2016*

This exhibition is the first solo show of Ania Jaworska, a trained architect and designer who explores the history of architecture and its relationship to society with two new projects. In the first one, Jaworska creates a site-specific installation of large, monochromatic black sculptures that reference common architectural elements such as arches, obelisks, gates, and signs. Set in a dark gallery space and removed from their traditional context of community, place, and time, the sculptures lose their symbolic importance and function. Her approach to the visual language of architecture is marked by humor and a use of bold, minimalist forms. The second project is a series of drawings commenting on the history and current state of columns, exploring their trajectory from symbols of power and status to open-ended forms often deployed with irony or cynicism. The exhibition is organized by Grace Deveney, the MCA Marjorie Susman Curatorial Fellow.

### JOHNSTON MARKLEE: GRID IS A GRID IS A GRID IS A GRID IS A GRID
*October 1, 2015 – January 3, 2016*

The Los Angeles-based architecture firm Johnston Marklee has been hired by the MCA to create a new master plan for the museum. Johnston Marklee have designed an intervention in the museum's current café space that refers to the grid of the building's original architect, Josef Paul Kleihues, and hints at some aspects of the renovations to come. Their immersive installation further emphasizes the proportions of the MCA's grid system by applying a repeating square graphic on the café walls, as well as creating a translucent ceiling plane that cuts the double-height space in half, hinting at a more intimate scale.

### POP ART DESIGN
*December 19, 2015 – March 27, 2016*

The Pop Art movement reflected on the cult of celebrity, commodity fetishism, and media reproduction that permeated everyday life in the postwar era and continues to shape our cultural understanding. A central characteristic of Pop Art was the dialogue between design and art, which is the focus in this exhibition—organized by the Vitra Design Museum, it is the first-ever comprehensive exhibition on the topic. Works by artists such as Andy Warhol, Claes Oldenburg, Roy Lichtenstein, and Judy Chicago are paired with design objects by Charles Eames, George Nelson, Achille Castiglioni, and Ettore Sottsass. This exhibition explores the relationship between everyday object and image, and shows how design was even, in some cases, the lead impetus in Pop Art.

# Chicago Architecture Foundation

Since 1966, CAF has served as a cultural ambassador of Chicago, using its architecture to inspire millions of visitors. This is accomplished through tours, programs, exhibitions, field trips, curricula, and online tools that are part of a dynamic learning journey for all ages.

*Address*
224 S. Michigan Ave.
Chicago, IL 60604

*Contact*
312-922-3432
architecture.org

**CHIDESIGN COMPETITION EXHIBITION: DESIGNING A CENTER FOR ARCHITECTURE, DESIGN AND EDUCATION**
*October 1, 2015 – January 3, 2016*

Capturing the spirit of the Biennial—and rekindling Chicago's history of significant competitions—the Chicago Architecture Foundation has sponsored an international ideas competition for the new Center for Architecture, Design, and Education (CADE). CADE will combine the new headquarters, visitor center, and exhibition spaces of the Chicago Architecture Foundation; a new headquarters for the Council on Tall Buildings and Urban Habitat; a design and allied arts high school; and flexible learning spaces for out-of-school-time youth programs. The curated shortlist of submissions is on display at this major exhibition.

**ARCHITECTURE IS ART**

In partnership with the Museum of Contemporary Art, the Chicago Architecture Foundation presents a set of two lectures with global designers who push the boundaries between architecture and art. The lectures are moderated by Reed Kroloff, CAF's senior advisor on Programs and Industry Collaboration.
Venue: Museum of Contemporary Art, 220 E Chicago Ave

Atelier Bow-Wow
*October 4, 2015*

Asymptote
*October 28, 2015*

# National Public Housing Museum + Temple Hoyne Buell Center for the Study of American Architecture at Columbia University

*Address*
1322 W. Taylor St.
Chicago, IL 60607

*Contact*
773-245-1621
nphm.org    buellcenter.org

### HOUSE HOUSING: AN UNTIMELY HISTORY OF ARCHITECTURE AND REAL ESTATE IN TWENTY-THREE EPISODES
Response by We, Next Door
*October 1, 2015 – November 15, 2015*

*House Housing: An Untimely History of Architecture and Real Estate* is an ongoing research project conducted by the Temple Hoyne Buell Center for the Study of American Architecture at Columbia University that encourages a public, historically informed conversation about the intersection of architecture and real estate development.

In Chicago, the Buell Center has teamed up with the National Public Housing Museum for an installation in two apartments within the former Jane Addams Homes. The exhibition *We, Next Door*, organized by NPHM with its Youth Advisory Council, responds creatively and critically to the *House Housing* episodes—situating the project specifically in Chicago and in the young people's lived experience of public housing.

Together, these exhibitions speak of a history that is untimely due to its ability to unsettle the present; their aim is that visitors discover a new perspective through which to see the architecture and real estate that surround us all.

Curatorial Team: Reinhold Martin (director, Buell Center), Todd Palmer (associate director and curator, National Public Housing Museum), Jacob Moore (curator and program coordinator, Buell Center), Susanne Schindler (curator and lead researcher, Buell Center); design: MTWTF

### ROUNDTABLE: THE FUTURE OF PUBLIC HOUSING
*November 9, 2015*

This roundtable convenes practitioners and public housing residents to discuss the future of housing as an infrastructure that demands greater allocation of public resources. Prospects for a more equitable housing future will be framed in light of current crises of debilitated public institutions and infrastructures, and take into account historical analyses of the market forces behind these conditions.

With Jennifer Scott, Charles Leeks, Reinhold Martin, Teresa Cordova, Rasmia Kirmani Frye, Crystal Palmer, Nadine Maleh (moderator)

# Rebuild Foundation

Photo: Tom Harris © Hedrich Blessing 2015

Rebuild Foundation is a not-for-profit creative engine initiated by Chicago-born artist Theaster Gates. It focuses on culture-driven redevelopment and affordable spaces in under-resourced communities and is currently managing a number of projects in the Greater Grand Crossing neighborhood of Chicago.

The organization's programs enlist teams of artists, architects, developers, educators, community activists, and residents who work together to integrate arts, training, and entrepreneurship into a community-driven process of neighborhood transformation and reuse of abandoned spaces.

*Contact*
312-857-5561
rebuild-foundation.org

Rebuild Foundation's sites can be visited during public programs and in the regularly scheduled public tours

*Rebuild Foundation's Sites*

**ARCHIVE HOUSE**
6916 S. Dorchester Ave.
Chicago, IL 60637

**LISTENING HOUSE**
6918 S. Dorchester Ave.
Chicago, IL 60637

**DORCHESTER ART + HOUSING COLLABORATIVE**
1456 E. 70th St.
Chicago, IL 60637

**BLACK CINEMA HOUSE**
7200 S. Kimbark Ave.
Chicago, IL 60619

**STONY ISLAND ARTS BANK**
6760 S. Stony Island Ave.
Chicago, IL 60649

# University of Chicago

Over the past 125 years, the University of Chicago in Hyde Park has evolved as a destination for art and architecture. The campus's earliest buildings in the neo-Gothic architectural style remain a trademark of the University and a symbol of its scholarly legacy, but the institution now also encompasses new buildings designed by some of the most innovative and renowned architects in the world.

*Address*
5801 S. Ellis Ave.
Chicago, IL 60637

*Contact*
773-702-2787
arts.uchicago.edu
urban.uchicago.edu
openhousechicago.org

During the Chicago Architecture Biennial, the University of Chicago will host a range of art and architecture exhibitions, programs, and performances, as well as tours of the campus.

JESSICA STOCKHOLDER: ROSE'S INCLINATION
*September 12, 2015 – July 2, 2017*
Smart Museum of Art

*Rose's Inclination* intersects the Smart Museum's lobby with a wave of color and texture that climbs to the clerestory, cuts across the floor, and travels outward into the Museum's sculpture garden.

KATARINA BURIN: PETRA ANDREJOVA-MOLNÁR —CONTRIBUTION AND COLLABORATION
*September 16 – November 13, 2015*
Neubauer Family Collegium for Culture and Society

An exhibition of work (in the form of architectural models, drawings, furniture and design objects, photographs, and texts) attributed to the fictional Czechoslovakian architect Petra-Andrejova Molnár, as realized by American artist Katarina Burin.

FORMS OF IMAGINATION
*September 18, 2015 – January 8, 2016*
Arts Incubator Gallery

*Forms of Imagination* exposes to the public the projects of a number of architecture studios participating in the design competition for the proposed Green Line Arts Center. The exhibit represents a variety of ways in which architecture impacts the Washington Park community, providing transparency on how ideas come to life.

SO-CALLED UTOPIAS
*November 20, 2015 – January 10, 2016*
Reva and David Logan Center for the Arts

*So-Called Utopias* is a group exhibition that examines the intersection of utopian visions with postcolonial and postindustrial sites. Traversing the dense forests of Amazonia to the urban sprawl of Bangalore, it presents such environments as an act of failure in the pursuit of expansionist and nationalist ideals. *So-Called Utopias* is curated by Yesomi Umolu.

VICTOR BURGIN: PRAIRIE
*November 20, 2015 – January 15, 2016*
Neubauer Family Collegium for Culture and Society

*Prairie* is a new digital projection work by Victor Burgin, created as part of Overlay, a collaborative research project by Burgin and D. N. Rodowick. *Prairie* responds to specific architectural sites (The Mecca apartment building and the IIT Crown Hall) to explore the erased or disappeared cultural histories inscribed in the built environment.

*The full program of exhibitions, events, and campus tours organized by the University of Chicago is available online.*

# School of the Art Institute of Chicago, AIADO

The Department of Architecture, Interior Architecture, and Designed Objects at the School of the Art Institute of Chicago incubates new practices that expand the range and purview of design. Taking advantage of its unique location in the Chicago Loop, and of the 150-year experimental legacy of fine-arts education at the School, the Department teaches designers to be critical, innovative, and activist in their practice.

*Address*
36 S. Wabash St.
Chicago, IL 60603

*Contact*
312-629-6650
saic.edu/academics/
departments/aiado/

## OUTSIDE DESIGN
*September 11 – December 11, 2015*

*Outside Design* explores the turn in art and design toward biotechnology and ecological systems. The show brings together five firms whose research-based work develops new knowledge at the edges of design practice. Analog Media Lab (Urbana-Champaign), Ants of the Prairie (Buffalo), The Living (New York), Species of Space (Chicago), and Sweet Water Foundation (Chicago) all pursue projects that move outside of their core of expertise and into the center of other fields.

Responding to these dialogic practices, the exhibition is organized as a series of laboratories installed across the galleries, engaged throughout the fall by students, faculty, and visiting artists and designers. This mode of collaborative experimentation and exchange continuously transforms the gallery space, resulting in new projects and installations and pushing disciplinary boundaries. An ambitious schedule of programs further activates the space, and connects it to local arts and design institutions.

*Outside Design* is curated by Jonathan Solomon, director of the Department of Architecture, Interior Architecture, and Designed Objects.

## PANEL: DEATH AND AFTERLIFE OF THE POSTINDUSTRIAL CITY
*September 30, 2015*

With Martino Stierli, Mechtild Widrich, Shiben Banerji, Jorge Otero-Pailos, Mabel Wilson

## LECTURE: KUNLÉ ADEYEMI
*October 5, 2015*

# IIT College of Architecture

Photo: Terrance Williams-Wundr Studio

The IIT College of Architecture welcomes students, faculty, and guests from around the globe who share an interest in rethinking the metropolis. With a history of design excellence and technical expertise and inspiring spaces in the S. R. Crown Hall (designed by Ludwig Mies van der Rohe), IIT Architecture is one of the most respected architecture schools in North America.

IIT Architecture's curriculum is structured around an innovative "horizontal cloud studio"—a school-wide design and research laboratory in which students from all degree programs work together on topics related to the metropolis.

Over the course of the Biennial, IIT Architecture hosts some of the world's leading architects through a program organized by the faculty and selected IIT partners (the Mies Crown Hall Americas Prize, the Council on Tall Buildings and Urban Habitat, the Mies van der Rohe Society, and the Louis Vuitton Spark Award).

Shows on the IIT campus include the projects nominated for the inaugural Mies Crown Hall Americas Prize, as well as the exhibition *Dialogues on Urbanization: Emerging Landscapes*, produced by the Master of Landscape Architecture program. The Mies Society is hosting artist Santiago Borja for a special event in Carr Chapel.

*Address*
S. R. Crown Hall
3360 S. State St.
Chicago, IL 60616

*Contact*
312-567-3230
arch.iit.edu

IIT ARCHITECTURE CHICAGO DEAN'S LECTURE SERIES:

Mels Crouwel (Benthem Crouwel Architects)
*October 7, 2015*

Susannah Drake (dlandstudio)
*November 4, 2015*

Erwin Olaf
*October 21, 2015*

Stefano Boeri (Stefano Boeri Architetti)
*November 11, 2015*

MIES CROWN HALL AMERICAS PRIZE LECTURE:

Jacques Herzog (Herzog & De Meuron)
*November 16, 2015*

# University of Illinois at Chicago, School of Architecture

The School of Architecture at UIC promotes architecture as a cultural practice of organizing information, of intelligently identifying and deploying patterns—conceptual, visual, structural, behavioral, and material—in the world. The program prepares its graduates to project all scales of these patterns through the systematic development of an aesthetic attitude, technical confidence, and a theoretical opportunism.

*Address*
3100 A+D Studios, MC030
845 W. Harrison St.
Chicago, IL 60607

*Contact*
312-996-3335
arch.uic.edu

PANEL: BETWEEN LOVE AND HATE
*November 12, 2015*

Never has architectural criticism been more needed than now. In an age of list-makers, networkers, formatters, and exhibitionists, in a situation where design values are no longer assumed or given, but need to be designed, the pleasures and discriminations of criticism need to be reasserted. Whether dismissed by critical history, or enthusiastically embraced by all-consuming curators, contemporary architectural practice is not being served well. A group of young writers and thinkers is asked to imagine, a posteriori, new zones of design criticism through three questions: what is being done, what is not being done, what is to be done?
Moderated by Penelope Dean, associate professor, UIC.

# Harris Theater for Music and Dance

The Joan W. and Irving B. Harris Theater for Music and Dance is a 1,500-seat performance venue located in Chicago's Millennium Park. Opened in November 2003, the nonprofit Harris Theater was the first multiuse performance space to have been built in downtown Chicago since 1929. Harris Theater serves as a unique national model of collaboration between the philanthropic community and performing arts organizations in music and dance.

*Address*
205 E. Randolph Dr.
Chicago, IL 60601

*Contact*
312-334-7777
harristheaterchicago.org

JESSICA LANG DANCE
*November 6, 2015*

Commissioned by the Harris Theater and the Chicago Architecture Biennial, American choreographer Jessica Lang creates a new dance for her company, Jessica Lang Dance, in collaboration with celebrated architect Steven Holl. In this new work, Lang takes a sculptural approach, using visually arresting sets and costumes, to enable three-dimensional interactions with bodies and objects, and evoke emotions and tangible sensation.

# Lampo

Lampo commissions, produces, and presents the work of leading music experimentalists. The organization presents seasons of concerts, bringing artists from around the world to Chicago, and supporting the creation and performance of new work. Founded in 1997, Lampo also organizes educational programs, maintains an archive, and publishes written and recorded documents related to its performance series.

*Contact*
312-297-7422
lampo.org

FLORIAN HECKER: REFORMULATIONS
*October 9, 2015*

Renowned artist and experimental musician Florian Hecker premieres *Reformulations*, an ambitious multichannel audio work offering a detailed sonic exploration of Preston Bradley Hall.

Venue: Preston Bradley Hall, Chicago Cultural Center

# Chicago Architectural Club

The Chicago Architectural Club provides an open forum for architects, artists, and writers to enrich the dialogue among practitioners and scholars. It hosts annually recurring competitions, lectures, and exhibitions that promote a younger generation of architects and designers.

*Contact*
773-517-4712
chicagoarchitecturalclub.org

2015 BURNHAM PRIZE COMPETITION:
CURRENCIES OF ARCHITECTURE EXHIBITION
*October 8, 2015 – January 3, 2016*

The 2015 Burnham Prize challenges participants to develop a single image that represents a strong point of view to explore the question, what is the State of the Art of Architecture today? The competition allows CAC to champion the work of a new generation of architects and foster vigorous debates on the fundamental issues of today's architecture.

Venue: Chicago Architecture Foundation

# Rhona Hoffman Gallery

**Address**
118 N. Peoria St.
Chicago, IL 60607

**Contact**
312-455-1990
rhoffmangallery.com

**JAMES WINES: DRAWINGS**
*October 2 – October 30, 2015*

James Wines is the founder and president of SITE, the former chair of Environmental Design at Parsons School of Design, and currently a professor of Architecture at Penn State University. He has given lectures at a large number of colleges, universities, and conferences. Among his publications are *De-Architecture* (Rizzoli, 1987) and *Green Architecture* (Taschen, 2000)

Wines has designed more than one hundred and fifty architecture, landscape, interior, and exhibition projects for both private and municipal clients. He received the 1995 Chrysler Award for Design Innovation, and fellowships from the National Endowment for the Arts, the Kress Foundation, the American Academy in Rome, the Guggenheim Foundation, the Rockefeller Foundation, the Graham Foundation, the Ford Foundation, and the Pulitzer Prize for Graphics.

# Volume Gallery

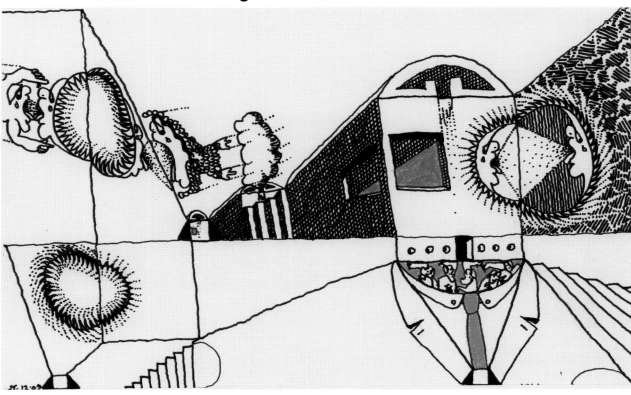

*Address*
845 W. Washington Blvd,
3rd Floor
Chicago, IL 60607

*Contact*
312-224-8683
wvvolumes.com

**STANLEY TIGERMAN: 821 STANLEY TIGERMAN SKETCHES**
*October 24 – December 5, 2015*

After visiting the first Architecture Biennale in Venice in 1980, Tigerman began a series of travel sketches that continue to this day. They are presented here alongside his architectural and "architoon" sketches. The juxtaposition reveals the mutual influence of different experiences, in a fascinating exploration into the mind of Tigerman and his architectural production in the last forty years.

A principal in the Chicago firm Tigerman McCurry and a fellow of the American Institute of Architects, Stanley Tigerman has thus far designed over 450 buildings and installations around the world, and was a founding member of the Chicago Seven.

# Chicago Design Museum

*Address*
108 N. State St., 3rd Floor
Chicago, IL 60602

*Contact*
312-894-6263
chidm.com

**NEW HORIZON: ARCHITECTURE FROM IRELAND**
*October 2, 2015 – January 2, 2016*

The Chicago Design Museum and Irish Design present *New Horizon: Architecture from Ireland*, an international extension of a year-long initiative exploring, promoting, and celebrating contemporary Irish design. It features installations by ten emerging architecture practices from Ireland across three global partner cities, London, Chicago, and Shenzhen.

In the gallery of the Chicago Design Museum, three Dublin-based firms—A2 Architects, GKMP Architects, and Ryan Kennihan—will create an intervention, part installation and part exhibition. The design concept pays tribute to Chicago's grid system established by Daniel Burnham, and to the world-famous architecture of Ludwig Mies van der Rohe. The physical expression of the installation features a mirrored ceiling that extends a supporting grid of I-beams to infinity. A large communal table, inspired by the traditional decorative arts of Ireland, will showcase the work of each firm.

Curated by Raymund Ryan and Nathalie Weadick.

# Chicago International Film Festival

Cinema/Chicago is a not-for-profit arts and education organization dedicated to encouraging better understanding between cultures and to making a positive contribution to the art form of the moving image. The Chicago International Film Festival is one of the year-round programs presented by Cinema/Chicago, and, celebrating its fifty-first anniversary, it is North America's longest-running competitive film festival.

*Contact*
312-683-0121
chicagofilmfestival.com

CHICAGO INTERNATIONAL FILM FESTIVAL SPOTLIGHT: ARCHITECTURE+SPACE+DESIGN
*October 15 – 29, 2015*

This program of architecture-themed and design-related films celebrates outstanding representations of innovative architecture and design in the cinema. From narrative features and documentaries to short films, the international selection features the work of celebrated designers (Michele De Lucchi, Gottfried Böhm, Bjarke Ingels) as well as chronicling ordinary people and characters interacting with extraordinary and complex places and spaces. The Spotlight also includes parallel programming, such as panel discussions and talks with directors, architects, and designers, fostering in-depth exploration of the connections between these arts.

ARCHITECTS ON FILM
*Most Wednesdays October 14 – December 9, 2015*

Local and visiting architects select and present a variety of films that have touched their lives and careers. The curated selection ranges from films that have been influential to an architect's thinking to those which are likely to spark a debate. Screenings are followed by conversations with presenters.

# SC Johnson

Photo: Historic American Buildings Survey, Library of Congress, 1969

Two buildings of the SC Johnson corporate campus in Racine, Wisconsin, were designed by Frank Lloyd Wright: the Administration Building, completed in 1939, and the Research Tower, completed in 1950. Wright's two buildings for SC Johnson are considered to be among the most relevant works in twentieth-century American architecture.

*Address*
1525 Howe St.
Racine, WI 53403

*Reservations*
scjohnson.com/visit

**TOUR OF SC JOHNSON'S CAMPUS AND WRIGHT-DESIGNED BUILDINGS**
*October 1 – January 3*
Thursday: 10 am – 5 pm; 3 pm – 11 pm
Friday: 10 am – 5 pm
Saturday and Sunday: 10 am – 6:30 pm

Every Thursday, Friday, Saturday, and Sunday throughout the Biennial, free shuttles transport visitors to Racine to explore Frank Lloyd Wright's SC Johnson corporate headquarters. The tour features the Administration Building and Research Tower as well as the newly refurbished 1940s office of SC Johnson's former president H. F. Johnson Jr. These are the only Wright-designed commercial buildings still in use. Weekend tours also include Wingspread, the home Wright designed for H. F. Johnson Jr. in the late 1930s. At 14,000 sq. ft. (1,300 m²), Wingspread is the last and largest of Wright's Prairie-style houses.

Shuttles depart from and return to the Chicago Cultural Center. Reservations are required.

# Farnsworth / National Trust for Historic Preservation

The National Trust for Historic Preservation, founded in 1949, is a privately funded nonprofit organization that works to save America's historic places.

*Address*
14520 River Rd.
Plano, IL 60545

*Contact*
630-552-0052
farnsworthhouse.org

**ARCHITECTURE + ART: INSPIRATION AMPLIFIED**
*October–November 2015*

Farnsworth (a site of the National Trust for Historic Preservation) and United States Artists (USA, the national Chicago-based organization dedicated to supporting accomplished and innovative American artists) have joined forces to create a public program for the Chicago Architecture Biennial. For *Architecture + Art: Inspiration Amplified*, two USA Fellows are creating new work inspired by the Farnsworth House and its landscape. The project demonstrates how the Farnsworth House, an exemplary representation of the International Style of architecture built in 1951 by Ludwig Mies van der Rohe, continues to inspire artists today. At the same time, the project showcases the opportunity for new and innovative arts programming at historic architectural sites.

Iñigo Manglano-Ovalle has a varied and complex practice that encompasses mostly sculpture and video. He often collaborates on projects that make abstractions tangible, tackling political issues such as immigration and climate change. Manglano-Ovalle is a professor in the Department of Art Theory and Practice at Northwestern University, Chicago, and won a MacArthur Fellowship in 2001.

Mary Ellen Childs composes concert work, often with a strong visual element, for a variety of instrumental ensembles. The creator of many multimedia projects, Childs is best known for her "visual percussion" pieces for her group CRASH, in which she incorporates the movement of the performers' bodies. Childs has received commissions from, among others, the Kronos Quartet, St. Paul Chamber Orchestra, the Kitchen, and the Walker Art Center.

# A HISTORY OF CHICAGO IN TEN ARCHITECTURES
## Alexander Eisenschmidt

Chicago is a young city. While in the early nineteenth century it was only a frontier village with a few settlers, it had materialized by 1870 as one of the largest markets in the world, supported by an unparalleled railroad junction and a harbor that connected the center of the US with the rest of the Western world and beyond. By 1890, its population had passed the one-million mark, and the city sprawled over more than 180 square miles, making it the largest urban footprint in North America. What made all of this possible was the implementation of the gridiron by James Thompson in 1830 on land south of the Chicago River. The grid laid the foundation, both figuratively and literally, for Chicago's rise as the archetypal metropolis. During its rapid expansion, the grid was quickly brought in line with the coordinates of the Land Ordinance of 1785 that defines much of the United States. As a result, Chicago's layout became the ultimate tool for infinite and rational urban export —an experiment that in its relentlessness made no concession to topography or beautification but became an instrument to organize land, mark progress, and structure architectural form. A nighttime view across the city makes this blatantly clear: the nonhierarchical avenues and streets run straight through the town, into the prairie, and continue their way across the US.

This kind of accelerated urban growth was encouraged by an unusual mix of optimism, pragmatism, and open-mindedness that became especially clear in moments of crisis, of which Chicago had plenty. The infamous fire of 1871, for example, decimated large parts of the city, but Chicagoans seemingly welcomed the prospect of a new town. An apparent failure of the city was quickly reversed into a projective reading of the future; residents apparently embraced their involuntary new urban beginning and, according to popular accounts, even declared that the city "could not afford to do without it." The *Chicago Tribune* wrote on March 30, 1873: "Chicago was set forward ten years by the fire." With the regulating spaces of the grid newly exposed and the rubble pushed into the lake to expand Chicago eastward, massive buildings began to emerge that soon lined entire blocks of the downtown grid turned vertical. The new building code, combining the advances in fireproof iron- and steel-frame construction with inventions such as Otis's safety elevator, contributed to remaking the city as a built experiment.

For early visitors, Chicago's development outpaced any reasonable idea of progress, with the future seemingly arriving in the present. This unlikely metropolis in the midwestern plains became the ideal forecaster of urbanities to come—an indicator of the fate of other cities. The sociologist Max Weber, for example, came to the city in 1904 in order to see what modern reality was like. Similarly to most visitors, he understood Chicago as the prototypical American city, the ur-metropolis, and, therefore, the ultimate launchpad for modernity. Indeed, Chicago's power as a transmitter of ideas about the modern city and its particular capacity to foment radical architectural and urban visions is legendary. One might recall the journeys of Adolf Loos and Frank Lloyd Wright: the former visited Chicago in 1893 to see the World's Columbian Exposition, while the latter abandoned his established life and practice when he left Chicago for Europe in 1909. Both acted as carriers of ideas: Loos absorbed the lessons of the so-called "Chicago School" and brought the ideas of Louis Sullivan to Europe, while Wright's Wasmuth Portfolio linked international modernism to the American Midwest. Eventually, Loos and Wright returned to Chicago with radical proposals for, respectively, the Tribune Tower of 1922 and the National Life Insurance Building of 1924. Not only did the city provide a critical impulse for their excursions—acting as an accelerator to the transmission of their agendas —but also offered solid ground for the projection of their speculative proposals.

Contemporary observers associated Chicago's power as a springboard for urban and architectural dreams with its commitment to commercial progress, openness to technological experimentation, and willingness to reinvent itself—qualities manifested in such projects as the raising of the city's ground plane in the 1860s, the reversing of the Chicago River in the 1890s, and the expansion of the city on landfill during the 1910s and 1920s. As such, we might consider Chicago an idea rather than just a locale—emphasizing the city as a construct that is effective beyond its own bounds, providing the ground for experimentation and releasing ideas into the urban and architectural ether. The list of "Chicagoisms" is long, and the directory of projects that propelled these concepts even longer. Yet because of the unusual compactness of its urban history, most of Chicago's buildings and urban projects carry a multitude of ideas fundamental to architectural and urban modernity. This text makes no attempt to account for all innovators, for chronology, or for completeness. It rather seeks to provide a list of projects that challenged architectural and urban conventions: not a "Top 10" but an alphabetical list of ten architectures that in their presence account for and speak about countless other projects—some constructed and others yet to come.

## 1. AUDITORIUM BUILDING
Adler & Sullivan, 1889
430 S. Michigan Ave.

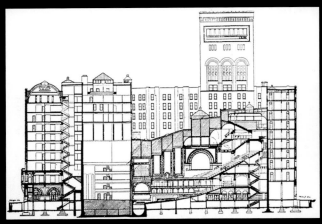

## 2. CHICAGO FEDERAL CENTER
Ludwig Mies van der Rohe, 1974
230 S. Dearborn St.

In 1901, Louis Sullivan writes in his *Kindergarten Chats* that Chicago's "architectural sins are unstable, captious and fleeting; it can pull itself down and rebuild itself in a generation ... it has done and can do great things when the mood is on. ... One must indeed be incurably optimistic, even momentarily, to dream such a dream." Sullivan hints here at the city's and his own predisposition toward optimism, at the potential of architecture as an organic expression of a democratic society, at Chicago's construction efforts after the fire, and at the massive buildings that emerged —of which the Auditorium Building is a particular specimen. The sheer size of the building, resulting from its programmatic complexity, made it the largest in the city. While the name originated from the sizeable auditorium of 6,000 seats for operas, the building also included a 500-room hotel with bars, restaurants, and banquet halls, as well as a business tract with twenty offices, ten banks, thirty studios, and shops that were to subsidize the theater. Much discussion has been devoted to Sullivan's idea of ornament and his façade treatments, yet the three-dimensional clustering of a multitude of vastly different functions into a spatial, programmatic figure and the appearance of this massive volume in the city deserve the same attention. The location of the different programs was linked to the city, where the hotel was oriented toward Michigan Avenue, the offices toward the commercial center, and the auditorium placed in between. In the midst of the building, however, programs spatially crossed, bypassed, and deviated, making a connection between façade and interior no longer possible. Today, one can still (unofficially) wander the building's interior complexities. Entering, for example, from Michigan Avenue and taking the elevator to the tenth floor of what is now the library of Roosevelt University, one emerges overlooking Grant Park and Lake Michigan.

In the dense center of Chicago, the Miesian urbanism of the Federal Center announces a different city—no longer solid street canyons carved into buildings but an open space punctured with individual objects. The contrast with the adjacent Monadnock building could not be more striking. Here, a thirty-story tower for courts and offices, a forty-two-floor tower for administration, and a one-story post office were carefully calibrated to organize two interlinking plazas. As one of Mies's later projects, it rehearses once more notions of urban composition, universal space, attempted clear-span, and curtain walls—all in one project this time. Thus, the Federal Center echoes earlier works such as IIT's Crown Hall and 860–880 Lake Shore Drive. While possibly less pure and more formulaic (after all, the post office is not a full-length free span, and Mies's staff had developed a rather expedited routine by the 1960s), it contributes a unique spatial experience to the city.

By leaving the ground floor of the office towers entirely open (only punctured by the lobbies with elevator shafts) and setting the glass back into the depth of the buildings, the ground opens up as a porous colonnade and enables views across the entire field of buildings. The pavement continues uninterrupted from plaza to lobby and back to the exterior, revealing the hovering, dark, and ghostly masses as shadows on the ground. At night, the optics reverse when the lobbies and the post office illuminate and glow like crystals on a continuous urban carpet. As elemental as each individual volume seems, the collective appearance of these prismatic objects is constantly shifting, from transparent to opaque, reflective to matte, aligned to disjointed, platonic to intricate. Here, Miesian cool turns into expressive urban forms—self-referential modernism into urban atmosphere.

154

## 3. CHICAGO RIVER
Isham Randolph and the Sanitary District of Chicago, 1900
Northern Branch Chicago River and Chicago Sanitary
and Ship Canal

## 4. IIT MCCORMICK TRIBUNE CAMPUS CENTER
Office for Metropolitan Architecture, 2003
3201 S. State St.

Shortly after 1900, Chicago became known as the city that made its river run uphill. The city had always discharged its waste into the Chicago River, which headed to Lake Michigan, increasing the risk of contaminating the source of the city's drinking water. In typical Chicago fashion, reversing the course of the river was proposed as a quick-fix solution to a larger ecological problem. Making Lake Michigan the river's source was first accomplished in 1871, when Chief Engineer Ellis Chesbrough (also responsible for Chicago's sewer system, the most comprehensive in the US) succeeded in reversing the river. Several months later, however, the sizable effort of dredging was negated as silt accumulated. Only through a large network of new water-ways and locks, the Sanitary and Ship Canal, did the city finally manage to change the flow of its river and, for the time being, send Chicago's waste water "upstream" and down the Mississippi. The canal enabled the city to continue its remarkable growth and became yet another instance of Chicago outpacing progress and forging ahead without much deliberation. The Chicago of the late nineteenth and early twentieth century was a laboratory and test-bed for speculation—ultimately, a city galvanized by crisis.

As the official story goes, OMA mapped student traffic between the dormitories and the academic buildings across the site (a former parking lot) and transcribed it into a one-story building that would consolidate different public functions, which were until then housed in multiple loca-tions across the IIT campus. Yet this low, contorted, and raw building is much more than an exercise in mapping. When passing through any of the entrances, where the campus grounds and the floor inside align smoothly, one is instantly propelled into a continuously expanding and con-tracting space. The flatness of the single floor suddenly emerges as a thick plan in which the ground occasionally dips down to form sunken areas for the cafeteria, computer stations, and lecture halls, intensified by a roof that cracks open to afford views out and light in. In the Campus Center, Adolf Loos's concept of *Raumplan* is played out in the flat-ness of the midwestern prairie—a spatial and geographical alchemy that references the low ceilings and expansive hori-zons of the homes by Frank Lloyd Wright as well as the porosity of Chicago below ground. The building is an unmis-takable product of Chicago, even if some of the city's architects had trouble recognizing it as such. Proposed as one of the first new buildings on Mies's legendary IIT campus after more than thirty years, OMA's design was des-tined to be controversial. And when the scheme proposed latching onto Mies's Commons Building, Chicago's preser-vationists and students of Mies were enraged. Apparently, the campus that had only been made possible by clear-ing sections of the dense fabric of the South Side was now to be left untouched. Apart from its conservatism, the argu-ment marks a misunderstanding of OMA's scheme as much as a misreading of Mies's campus design. Unlike a tradi-tional campus, Mies saw his design as neither closed off from the outside nor a complete composition. More impor-tantly, OMA's design has the potential to turn the tables on the previous expansionist mentalities of IIT and invite inhabitants from the surrounding neighborhoods in.

## 5. JOHN HANCOCK TOWER
Skidmore, Owings & Merrill, 1970
875 N. Michigan Ave.

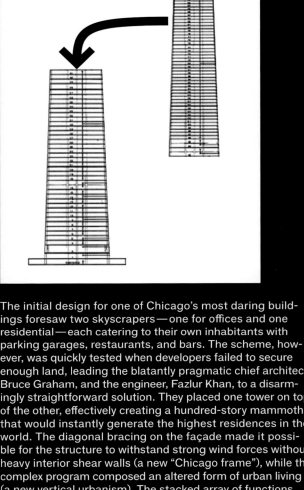

## 6. "L"
Northwestern Elevated Railroad, 1897
Along Lake Street, Van Buren Street, Wells Street,
and Wabash Avenue

The initial design for one of Chicago's most daring build-ings foresaw two skyscrapers—one for offices and one residential—each catering to their own inhabitants with parking garages, restaurants, and bars. The scheme, how-ever, was quickly tested when developers failed to secure enough land, leading the blatantly pragmatic chief architect, Bruce Graham, and the engineer, Fazlur Khan, to a disarm-ingly straightforward solution. They placed one tower on top of the other, effectively creating a hundred-story mammoth that would instantly generate the highest residences in the world. The diagonal bracing on the façade made it possi-ble for the structure to withstand strong wind forces without heavy interior shear walls (a new "Chicago frame"), while the complex program composed an altered form of urban living (a new vertical urbanism). The stacked array of functions comprises several floors of shops at the bottom (some below and some above ground), parking for more then seven hun-dred cars up to the twelfth floor, twenty-eight floors of office space, and a residential lobby on the forty-fourth floor that caters to the 703 apartments above, topped by an obser-vation deck, restaurant, bar, and TV station—all wrapped into a new structural frame. A high-speed elevator creates a shortcut between the sidewalk and the apartments —bypassing the garage and the offices, and catapulting the tenants directly into the "sky-lobby" with its mailboxes, conference rooms, supermarket, dry cleaner, gymnasium, and swimming pool. By placing one skyscraper on top of another, the common logic of the generic tower was questioned, creating a new architectural species that inten-sifies and accelerates the conditions of the stand-alone tall building. Here, metropolitan lifestyle confronts gated

The commercial center of Chicago became known as the Loop in the 1880s, when horse carriages and cable cars encircled the business district connecting the residential neighborhoods to the core of the city. This movement traced a new logistical space that soon manifested with the con-struction of the Union Loop railroad on elevated tracks. As the first trains traveled along the half-mile square between the streets of Lake, Van Buren, Wells, and Wabash Avenue, they carved a new infrastructural space into the massive urban blocks of office buildings and stores. In the process, they intensified the city's pulsations and made readable a new commercial zone in the middle of the city. During these years, the multistory office buildings and department stores grew not only in height but also in volume. Some took over entire blocks and others extended their reach by linking to adjacent buildings or train stops close by. The Schlesinger and Mayer Store (later the Carson Pirie Scott by Louis Sullivan) famously connected to the elevated train via a glassed cast-iron bridge on Wabash Avenue, in an effort to link the store and the region. While the street traffic entered on the ground level, travelers by train accessed the store directly at the second floor, where the flows of the city fused with the currents of the interior. Today, buildings such as the Merchandise Mart or the Helmut Jahn–designed Thompson Center connect seam-lessly to the "L," as the elevated train was eventually called. Those infrastructural connections might give us a taste of the pandemonium of traffic that ruled the raw capitalism of late nineteenth-century Chicago, as long as we keep in mind that the intertwined pedestrian, rail, and horse traffic of the past

## 7. MARINA CITY
Bertrand Goldberg, 1967
300 N. State St.

## 8. MONADNOCK BUILDING
Burnham & Root, 1891, and Holabird & Roche, 1893
53 W. Jackson Blvd.

As in many other cities across the US, the postwar flight to the suburbs and the concept of urban centers as business zones had left Chicago's downtown largely bereft of residential living by the 1960s. In this context, Bertrand Goldberg performed a kind of coup d'etat on the city. As he said in a 1992 interview for the Chicago Architects Oral History Project, "I knew I had to design something that had far greater efficiency than anything that had been done before, because I had to design for low rents. In order to induce people to live downtown, I had to have an exciting environment —a total environment." Indeed, the compound was understood as a city within a city, an array of urban microclimates that together form an urban composite. The original Marina City integrated two residential sixty-story towers with nineteen floors of parking, a sixteen-floor office building with a bowling alley, a swimming pool, a theater, and a three-story podium that housed an ice-skating rink, stores, and a marina below. Not only did the project include components that suburbia did not possess but it also condensed the city into a complex amalgam of programs in which the plinth acts as connective tissue between water, subterranean streets, pedestrian flow, car traffic, and parking as well as the theater, offices, and housing towers that plug in from above. While in the depths of the base the different programs blend into each other, the structures above are clear objects in the city. This first became notable when the residential towers were built in parallel by cranes that layered the floral patterns of the apartment layouts, eventually creating the unmistakable vibrancy of the exterior. And, when we see today the towers reflected in the adjacent IBM Building by Mies van der Rohe, the tension between the two ideologies could not be more dramatic.

Circa 1890, John Wellborn Root, of Burnham & Root, spoke during a lecture of an "America [that is] free of artistic traditions. Our freedom begets license, it's true. We do shocking things, we produce works of architecture … irredeemably bad; we try crude experiments that result in disaster. Yet somehow in this mass of ungoverned energies lies the principle of life." For him, Chicago's lack of history was associated with the freedom to surpass established norms and conventions. It was an urban climate where metropolitan pressures had impaired artistic and stylistic traditions, making a new simplicity and monumentality possible—pressures that, in the case of the early Monadnock, even its architects had to catch up to. After a draftsman was instructed to prepare a version of the façade devoid of ornamentation in order to save money, Root was apparently shocked at the sight of what he called a "brick box." The architects had unintentionally created a new building paradigm that they could no longer recognize. However, the project that Root initially perceived as an architectural "outcast" and had to come to terms with would set later generations of architects free, as they began to identify the building as a powerful blend of forces assembled from the laboratory of the modern city. Ludwig Hilberseimer, for example, admired the building slab in his *Großstadtarchitektur* for its "unmistakable sense of proportion." In addition, the extension of the block to the south marked the transition from load-bearing walls to steel-frame construction. Its completion in 1893 marked a decisive moment in architectural history: the Monadnock was at once evidence of this transition and one of the last buildings of its typology. When the World's Columbian Exposition opened in the same year on Chicago's South Side, its white-painted, unified civic image questioned the laissez-faire development of the skyscraper city and helped to establish a height limit of 130 feet. Between the Exposition, the emergence of city planning as a profession, the new agendas of the City Beautiful movement, and Burnham and Bennett's *Plan of Chicago*, the fate of that short-lived heroic period was sealed. The idea of the tower as an object in the city only resurfaced in the 1920s with the launch of the Tribune Tower competition. By that time, Loos, Saarinen, Taut, and Hilberseimer had channeled the ingenuities of the Monadnock block into competition projects that far outpaced the building that was eventually constructed.

## 9. PEDWAY
Chicago Department of Transportation, 1951-today
Bordered by Kinzie Street, Field Drive, Congress Parkway,
and Clinton Street

Chicago's massive urban blocks are contrasted by an
intense porosity below ground. After the raising of the
city's grounds by an average of ten feet to avoid flooding
in the mid-nineteenth century, and the burrowing of Lower
Wacker as a service road into the River's edge during the
1920s, Chicago's multilevel cavernousness was extended
from an initial tunnel that served as shortcut between two
subway lines (Red and Blue, between the Washington and
Jackson stops). Soon, this underground pedestrian network
started to expand as a connective tissue across forty blocks
via tunnels and bridges, eventually amounting to almost six
miles of walkways that had become an urbanism in their
own right, a kind of interior city that expands the traditional
dichotomies of exterior and interior, public and private, corporate and communal, individual and collective. Here, the
Parisian Arcades found their natural continuation by leaving
the urban block intact but excavating the ground to increase
the occupiable volume. The textures of this infrastructure
in the guts of the city shift ever so often, from train stations to hotel lobbies, parking lots, malls, restaurants, and
swimming pools. For example, when entering the Pedway
through the elevator in the Cultural Center's Randolph street
entrance, and walking toward Daniel Burnham's Marshall
Field's department store (today Macy's), one encounters
a purified oasis amid pedestrian traffic. Separated only
by a few layers of glass, girls in bikinis and older men
in Speedos seem to be standing on the subterranean sidewalk to take a dip.

## 10. ROBIE HOUSE
Frank Lloyd Wright, 1909
5757 S. Woodlawn Ave.

While Burnham and Sullivan were devoted to shaping the
environment of the city, Wright's buildings formed the architectural perception of what Chicago's suburbs could look
like. In Oak Park alone, Wright designed and built more than
twenty structures between 1889 and 1913. Under the spiritual leadership of Sullivan (for whom Wright worked for
several years), influenced by the Arts and Crafts tradition,
and in contact with the radical circles of the Hull House community, Wright developed a domestic architecture of rural
innocence that spoke most clearly to the flatness of the midwestern prairie and remained skeptical of the metropolis.
Abstracting the walls and roofs into intersecting planes not
only created a fluid interior but also radically blurred the line
to the exterior. The openness of the Robie House, where the
roofs seem to float above the terraces, is no graphic trick-
ery but the result of steel beams in the ceiling that carry all
of the cantilever's weight. What at first sight might appear
as an innocent exploration of idyllic living is, in fact, a technologically enhanced machine—advancing the Domino
scheme even before its conception. For Wright, the effort
of deploying the Chicago frame for a single home was cer-
tainly worthwhile. Drawings of the house were published
in the legendary Wasmuth portfolio, which Wright used for
orchestrating a redirection of his career, and which would
change the course of European architecture.

## +1. JANE BYRNE (CIRCLE) INTERCHANGE
Illinois Department of Transportation, 1962
Junction of I-90, I-94, and I-290

At the geographic center of the city there exists an infrastructural experiment. What Daniel Burnham had previously
envisioned as a cultural civic center in his *Plan of Chicago*
is today the Circle Interchange—a complex knot of road
and rail intersections, formed by the Congress Parkway,
three expressways (Dan Ryan, Eisenhower, and Kennedy),
and pierced by the city's Blue Line train, which transitions
here from surface operation to subway. The hybrid states
of mobility are set square into the city. Three hundred thou-
sand vehicles converge daily and take part in a collective
event, a manifestation of the distortions of time and space.
While the interchange is a product of rational engineering
and purposeful machining, solely driven by the ambition to smooth out the discontinuities between different
flows of traffic, it bears daily witness to some of the city's
slowest vehicular travel. With a combined loss estimated
at twenty-five million hours per year, it ranks as the most
congested freight bottleneck in the nation. But while the
Circle Interchange uproots and reverses its initial premise,
it hovers bizzarely between the "civilized" urbanism of housing and education around it and the "advanced" urbanism
of infrastructure it aspires to. This spatial concoction might
be the city's most powerful non sequitur.

# PARTICIPANTS

3D DESIGN STUDIO was established in 1997 by A. Melinda Palmore and Darryl G. Crosby in order to pursue their desire to bring a renewed energy and design philosophy to projects responding to urban and inner city environments. The firm won the Universal and Affordable House Competition, sponsored by the City of Chicago in 2002. Current projects include a new lounge for the Goodman Theater, and the Intergenerational Learning Center in Chicago.

AL BORDE was founded by David Barragán and Pascual Gangotena in 2007 in Quito, Ecuador. The other principals are Esteban Benavides and Malu Borja, both of whom joined the firm in 2010. Al Borde often works on projects with low budgets; they attempt to turn scarcity of resources into an advantage, considering not just money but also skills, knowledge, materials, property, or even friends and acquaintances as assets in the project. They have built several houses and community projects in Ecuador, such as the *Nueva Esperanza* school (2009), and they regularly organize construction workshops.

ALEXANDER EISENSCHMIDT is a designer, theorist, and assistant professor at the School of Architecture, University of Illinois at Chicago. He recently edited the book *Chicagoisms* (Scheidegger & Spiess / Park Books, 2013) and co-curated an exhibition of the same name at the Art Institute of Chicago in 2014. He is a partner in the design practice Studio Offshore and director of the Visionary Cities Project.

ALL(ZONE) is a group of architecture and design professionals based in Bangkok, led by Rachaporn Choochuey and Sorawit Klaimak. They are fascinated by their ever-changing metropolis, and the forms it gives to everyday life. All(zone) observes contemporary vernacular design solutions carefully and tries to learn from them.

AMANDA WILLIAMS has been consumed, for nearly twenty years, with how combining art and architecture might help make all parts of the city thrive, and understanding the relationship of color, race, and space. Color is a central preoccupation in her work, with an evolving palette derived from the urban landscapes she traversed as a child growing up in the Chicago neighborhood of Auburn Gresham. She is a 3Arts Foundation awardee, and recipient of a Joyce Foundation scholarship. Williams has exhibited and lectured throughout the US, including the Studio Museum in Harlem, and the Yerba Buena Center for the Arts. Williams is an adjunct professor at the Illinois Institute of Technology.

ANDREAS ANGELIDAKIS trained as an architect at Columbia University. He switches roles between artist, curator, and architect, and often reverses the expected sequence of architecture—realization to representation—by starting with an existing building and producing models, films, ruins, installations, or alternative histories, blurring fact and fiction, and smoothing out the borders between the real and the virtual. He is inspired by the city of Athens and his work deals with the notion of ruin, be it ancient, contemporary, or imaginary. Recent exhibitions include *The System of Objects*: *The Dakis Joannou Collection Reloaded by Andreas Angelidakis* at the DESTE Foundation, Athens (2013); *Every End Is a Beginning* at the National Museum of Contemporary Art, Athens (2014); and *Fin de Siècle* at the Swiss Institute, New York (2014).

ANDRÉS JAQUE is founder of the OFFICE FOR POLITICAL INNOVATION, a practice that develops architectural projects using research, performance, and installations. *Ikea Disobedients* is the first architectural performance to have been acquired by the Museum of Modern Art, New York. The practice received the Silver Lion for the best research at the Venice Architecture Biennale in 2014 for *SALES ODDITY: Milano 2 and the Politics of Direct-to-Home TV Urbanism*. Jaque is visiting professor at Princeton University's School of Architecture, and professor of Advanced Design at Columbia University's GSAPP.

ANIA JAWORSKA is an architect and educator. She is visiting assistant professor at the University of Illinois at Chicago, School of Architecture. Her practice focuses on exploring the connection between art and architecture with bold simple forms, humor, commentary and conceptual, historic, and cultural references. Jaworska's work was presented as part of Grounds for Detroit in the 2012 Venice Architecture Biennale, and in the *CHGO DSGN* exhibition at the Chicago Cultural Center in 2014. Jaowrska designed the Graham Foundation's bookshop in Chicago.

ANNE LACATON and JEAN-PHILIPPE VASSAL founded Lacaton & Vassal in 1987, a Paris-based practice that works on public buildings, housing, and urban planning. Their major projects include FRAC in Dunkirk, France, the renovation of Palais de Tokyo, Paris, and the transformation of several public housing estates in France.
FRÉDÉRIC DRUOT established his eponymous architectural agency in 1992. Its main activities are in housing, workplaces, and cultural venues, where it undertakes research into the altering of context, scale, and cost effectiveness in new buildings, as well as the transformation of pre existing ones.

ARANDA\LASCH is a New York and Tucson-based design studio dedicated to experimental research and innovative building. Established in 2003 by Benjamin Aranda and Chris Lasch, they have been recipients of the United States Artists Award and the Young Architects + Designers Award in 2007, the *Architectural Record* Design Vanguard Award in 2014, and the Architectural League Emerging

Voices Award in 2015. Current projects include three retail and civic buildings in Miami, Florida, a banquet hall and outdoor theater in Libreville, Gabon, and an arts center with an outdoor sculpture park, museum, and artist residences in Bali, Indonesia.

ARCHITECTEN DE VYLDER VINCK TAILLIEU is a practice based in Ghent, Belgium, where much of their built projects are located. With a focus on the renovation of houses and existing buildings, their architecture plays with the boundaries of discipline, manipulating materials and expectations. In the spring of 2015, their work was displayed in an exhibition design at ETH Zürich. Jan de Vylder is on the faculty at the University of Leuven, Belgium. Inge Vinck has taught at Accademia di Architettura in Mendrisio, Switzerland, and at ENSAPL Lille in France.

ASSAF EVRON's photographs and photo-based work focus on the structures and forms of the overlooked, revealing a visual state of both excess and deficiency. Evron earned an MFA from the School of the Art Institute of Chicago and a masters degree from the Cohn Institute for the History and Philosophy of Science and Ideas at Tel Aviv University. His commissions include the Israeli Pavilion at the 12th Venice Architecture Biennale, and the reinvention of the Dov Karmi Exhibition at the Tel Aviv Museum of Art. He has been awarded the Gerard Levy Prize by the Israel Museum in 2012, and the Israeli Ministry of Culture and Education Prize for Young Artists in 2010.

ASSEMBLE is a design and architecture practice based in London. Established in 2010 to undertake a single self-built project, Assemble has developed into a diverse practice while maintaining a cooperative structure. Their work focuses on using design as a tool to improve social and cultural life, with projects such as the renovation of New Addington square in South London. They have been nominated for the 2015 Turner Prize.

ATELIER BOW-WOW is a Tokyo-based firm founded by Yoshiharu Tsukamoto and Momoyo Kaijima in 1992. The pair's interests range from architectural design and urban research to the creation of public artworks, which are produced based on the concept of "behaviorology." Atelier Bow-Wow has designed and built houses and public buildings both in Tokyo and in Europe and the US. Their urban research led to the experimental project Micro-Public-Space, which has been exhibited across the world. Among their books are *Graphic Anatomy* (TOTO, 2007) and *Behaviorology* (Rizzoli, 2010).

BARBARA KASTEN received her BFA from the University of Arizona, Tucson, in 1959 and her MFA from the California College of Arts and Crafts, Oakland, in 1970. Based in Chicago, she has had solo exhibitions at institutions such as the George Eastman House, International Museum of Photography and Film, Rochester; the San Francisco Museum of Modern Art; and the International Center of Photography, New York. Her work is in numerous museum collections, including the Museum of Modern Art, New York; the Whitney Museum of American Art, New York; the Museum of Contemporary Art, Chicago; and the Los Angeles County Museum of Art.

BAUKUH is an architecture firm based in Milan and Genoa, Italy. Established in 2004, it is headed by Paolo Carpi, Silvia Lupi, Vittorio Pizzigoni, Giacomo Summa, Pier Paolo Tamburelli, and Andrea Zanderigo. Together they are founding editors of the journal *San Rocco*, and their writings have been published extensively. Baukuh designed and built Casa della Memoria in Milan, which was inaugurated in April 2015.

YELLOWOFFICE is an architectural studio in Milan focusing on landscape design and urbanism, led by Francesca Benedetto since 2008.

STEFANO GRAZIANI is a photographer who has collaborated with several architects including Office KGDVS, 51N4E, and Christ&Gantenbein; his recent publications include *Late Night Conversations* (Quodlibet, 2014).

BESLER & SONS was founded by Erin and Ian Besler in Los Angeles. She is a faculty member at UCLA's Department of Architecture and Urban Design. Prior to this, she has worked for Tigerman McCurry Architects and VOA Associates in Chicago, and First Office and Zago Architecture in Los Angeles. Her work has been presented as part of Beijing Design Week and has been exhibited widely in Los Angeles.

ATLV is a collaborative computational design studio founded in 2012 by Satoru Sugihara, a faculty member at SCI-Arc, Los Angeles.

BIG (Bjarke Ingels Group) is a Copenhagen- and New York-based group of architects, designers, builders, and thinkers. The office is currently involved in a large number of international projects, including West 57 in New York City and the new Google headquarters in Mountain View. Bjarke Ingels started BIG in 2005 after co-founding PLOT Architects in 2001 and working at OMA in Rotterdam. Ingels has received numerous awards and honors, including the RIBA and Holcim Awards in 2014, Danish Crown Prince's Culture Prize in 2011 and the Golden Lion at the Venice Biennale in 2004. In 2012, the American Institute of Architects granted the 8 House in Copenhagen its Honor Award, calling it "a complex and exemplary project of a new typology."

BRYONY ROBERTS is the principal of the design and research practice Bryony Roberts Studio, based in Los Angeles and Oslo. She worked in the offices of WORKac and Mansilla + Tunon before founding her own practice in 2011. Her studio focuses on transformations of historical architecture, with projects spanning installations, residential architecture, and urban design. Roberts recently guest-edited *Log 31: New Ancients* with Dora Epstein Jones. She has taught at Rice University School of Architecture in Houston and SCI-Arc in Los Angeles, and is now assistant professor at the Oslo School of Architecture.

The SOUTH SHORE DRILL TEAM is an organization established in 1980, which uses performing arts to engage young people at risk in the South Side of Chicago.

BUREAU SPECTACULAR, led by Jimenez Lai, imagines other worlds and engages with architecture through stories: beautiful ones about character development, relationships, curiosities and attitudes, and absurd ones about fake realities that invite enticing possibilities. The stories conflate design, representation, theory, criticism, history, and taste into cartoon pages, which swerve into the physical world through architectural installations, models, and small buildings. Bureau

Spectacular's installation, White Elephant, is in the collection of the Museum of Modern Art, New York. The studio designed the Taiwan Pavilion at the Venice Architecture Biennale in 2014.

CARLOS BUNGA is a Portuguese artist based in Barcelona. Originally trained as a painter, Bunga experiments with a variety of media, including sculpture, performance, and video. He often works with everyday materials to create installations at the architectural scale. Bunga has had several solo shows, including at Museu Serralves in Porto (2012), the Hammer Museum in Los Angeles (2011), and MACBA in Barcelona (forthcoming).

CENTRAL STANDARD OFFICE OF DESIGN's work employs physical forces (gravity, weight, temperature, weather patterns) and urban dynamics (crowds, human interaction, context/history) to elicit experiences as strange as they are familiar. It is directed by Kelly Bair, and received several awards including the Luvo International Design Competition, and the UIC Dean's Research Prize in 2015. Blair is currently assistant professor at the University of Illinois at Chicago.

COUNTERSPACE is a Johannesburg-based collaborative studio of young architecture graduates, established in 2014 by Sumayya Vally, Sarah de Villiers, and Amina Kaskar. Counterspace is dedicated to research-based projects, which take the form of exhibition design, competition work, urban insurgency, and public events. Their work is predominantly concerned with ideas for the future and otherness; it plays with image and narrative as a means of deconstructing and reconstructing space and city, and aims to incite provocative thought around perceptions of Johannesburg.

CSUTORAS & LIANDO is an architecture and design office led by Melissa Liando and Laszlo Csutoras, with offices in Jakarta and London. The office works at different scales—from one-off joinery to large-scale public buildings—and in different continents and cultural environments. Besides permanent architecture, they created temporary public spaces such as Kineforum Misbar, a free movie theater in Jakarta that has now become a regular annual event supported by the city. The firm is currently

working on a pavilion intended to revitalize Jakarta's dilapidated old town area.

DAAR (Decolonizing Architecture Art Residency) is an architectural collective based in Beit Sahour, Palestine. Co-founded by Alessandro Petti and Sandi Hilal, DAAR's work combines conceptual speculations, actual spatial interventions, discourse, and collective learning. DAAR aims to use spatial practice as a form of political intervention, exploring possibilities for the reuse, subversion, and profanation of actual structures of domination: from evacuated military bases to refugee camps, from uncompleted governmental structures to the remains of destroyed villages. The residency program gathers together architects, artists, activists, urban designers, filmmakers, and curators, to work collectively on the subject of politics and architecture. They recently authored, with Eyal Weizman, *Architecture after Revolution* (Sternberg Press, 2014).

DAVID BROWN's current design research, writing, and teaching explore process-oriented approaches to urban design and the city. Brown is author of *Noise Orders: Jazz, Improvisation, and Architecture* (University of Minnesota Press, 2006), a study of the design implications of structures that facilitate improvisation in jazz, and co-edited *Row: Trajectories through the Shotgun House* (Architecture at Rice, 2004). He is associate professor and associate director at the University of Illinois at Chicago's School of Architecture.

DAVID SCHALLIOL is a doctoral candidate at the University of Chicago's Department of Sociology. His work explores the transformation of urban centers through hybrid ethnographic, filmic, and photographic projects. His writing and photographs have appeared in such publications as the *Design Observer*, *The New York Times*, and *The American Sociologist*, as well as in numerous exhibitions. His first book, *Isolated Building Studies* (Utakatado, 2014) is a photographic exploration of Chicago's infrastructure, addressing the impact of investment processes on the urban community. He is currently making an ethnographic film about the displacement of more than 400 families in the South Side of Chicago.

DEANE SIMPSON is an architect, urbanist, and educator. He is associate professor at the Royal Danish Academy in Copenhagen, where he leads, with Charles Bessard, the international masters program Urbanism and Societal Change. He was formerly unit master at the Architectural Association, London; professor at BAS Bergen; associate at Diller Scofidio + Renfro, New York; and faculty member at the ETH Zürich. His research focuses on the architectural and urban implications of demographic change, and he is currently co-editing the books *Atlas of the Copenhagens* (Ruby Press, 2016) and *The City between Democracy and Security* (Birkhäuser, 2016).

DESIGN WITH COMPANY (Dw/Co) is the Chicago-based architectural collaborative of Stewart Hicks and Allison Newmeyer. Dw/Co seeks to transform the world through textual and visual narratives, speculative urban scenarios, installations, and small-scale interactive constructions. Hicks is currently an assistant professor of architecture at the University of Illinois at Chicago. Newmeyer is a visiting assistant professor at the University of Illinois at Chicago and also teaches at the University of Wisconsin, Milwaukee, and the Illinois Institute of Technology, Chicago. Both of them are fellows of the MacDowell Artist Colony and recipients of *Architectural Record*'s Design Vanguard Award and the Young Architect's Forum Prize.

DIDIER FAUSTINO is an artist and architect who works on the intimate relationship between body and space. His approach is multifaceted, from the creation of visual art to the design of spaces that exacerbate the senses. Prominent projects include *Body in Transit*, which is in the collection of the Centre Pompidou, Paris, and *Double Happiness*, presented at the Hong Kong/Shenzhen Bi-city Biennale in 2009. Faustino received the Académie d'Architecture's Dejean Prize for Lifetime Achievement in 2010. He is currently working on prestigious architectural projects around the world, including a library and a cultural center in Mexico and an experimental house in Spain for the curatorial series Solo Houses.

EL EQUIPO DE MAZZANTI was founded by Giancarlo Mazzanti in 2005. Based in Bogotá, Colombia, the studio's projects aim to be triggers for change, embracing place, renovating public space, activating the economy, creating opportunities for continuous learning, and promoting social inclusion and equity. Among their completed projects are the Biblioteca España (2007) and the Sports Coliseum (2009) in Medellín.

NICOLAS PARÍS is an artist and educator living in Bogotá.

FAKE INDUSTRIES ARCHITECTURAL AGONISM (FKAA) is an entity of variable boundaries and questionable taste that provides architectural tools to mediate between citizens and institutions, the public sphere, and disciplinary knowledge. Created by Cristina Goberna and Urtzi Grau from their headquarters in New York, Sydney, and Barcelona, FKAA bridges professional and academic worlds in an effort to reclaim the architect's role as a public intellectual—that is, someone who earnestly risks his or her credibility to question hegemonic beliefs. FKAA is currently completing the Velodrome of Medellín, the Superphosphates! Masterplan in Cáceres, and the OE House in Barcelona.

FALA ATELIER was founded in 2013 by Filipe Magalhães, Ana Luisa Soares, and Ahmed Belkhodja and is based in Porto, Portugal. The Atelier works with methodic optimism on a wide range of projects, from territories to birdhouses. Fala is also participating in *Unfeasible: Limit, Check, Opening*, a forthcoming architecture and design show at Systems Project in London.

FRIDA ESCOBEDO has been working as an independent architect in Mexico City since 2006. The projects her studio works on stand plainly for what they are: raw, clarified, left open to physical transformation and cultural differentiation. Conceptual works such as *Split Subject*, the El Eco pavilion, and *Civic Stag* address time not as a historical calibration but rather as a social operation. Escobedo's projects were presented in the Mexican Pavilion at the Venice Architecture Biennale in 2012, and she had her first solo exhibition at LIGA Espacio Para Arquitectura in Mexico City in the same year. In 2014, one of Escobedo's buildings, La Tallera Siqueiros, was nominated for the Design of the Year award at the Design Museum, London, and she participated in the Swiss Pavilion at the Venice Architecture Biennale.

Fabio GRAMAZIO and Matthias KOHLER founded the architecture practice Gramazio Kohler Architects in 2000. Their research merges advanced architectural design and additive robotic fabrication. Together with leading researchers in architecture, material sciences, computation, and robotics, Gramazio and Kohler have opened the world's first architectural robotic laboratory at ETH Zürich. Their work has been published extensively and displayed in venues such as the Venice Architecture Biennale, the Storefront for Art and Architecture, and the FRAC Centre.

The MIT SELF-ASSEMBLY LAB, directed by Skylar Tibbits, focuses on self-assembly and programmable material technologies for novel manufacturing, production, and construction processes. The lab is looking at potential applications for the manufacturing process across a wide range of disciplines, including biology, material science, software, robotics, manufacturing, transportation, infrastructure, construction, the arts, and even space exploration.

HINTERLANDS URBANISM AND LANDSCAPE is a Chicago-based research and design office founded in 2014 by Conor O'Shea, who is currently visiting assistant professor at the IIT College of Architecture. Hinterlands' recent projects include the Maumee Spit, a proposal to harness Toledo's Maumee river to create a sediment economy, and Logistical Urbanism, a plan to recalibrate freight infrastructure to twenty-first-century Chicago.

INDEPENDENT ARCHITECTURE was founded by Paul Andersen in 2009. Andersen also teaches at the University of Illinois at Chicago, and is the author of *The Architecture of Patterns* (2010) and *The Monuments Power the Cars* (2015).

PAUL PREISSNER runs Paul Preissner Architects and is associate professor at the School of Architecture at the University of Illinois at Chicago. Andersen and Preissner started their collaboration by designing two barns for the 2013 Biennial of the Americas.

IWAN BAAN is a Dutch photographer known for portraying the human life and interactions that take place within buildings. After some experience in publishing and documentary photography, he began collaborating with many of the world's leading

architectural firms, including OMA, Herzog & De Meuron, and Toyo Ito. A relentless traveler, Baan is currently one of the most published photographers in the field of architecture; his photographs have appeared in *Domus* and *The New York Times*, among many other publications. In 2010, he won the Julius Shulman Photography Award. Among his published books is *Brasilia-Chandigarh: Living with Modernity* (Lars Müller, 2010).

JAHN is an architecture firm founded in Chicago and currently operating four international offices. With over 75 years of experience, it has achieved critical recognition and won numerous awards. Under the current leadership of Helmut Jahn and Francisco Gonzalez-Pulido, the firm has grown steadily from the practice founded in 1937 by Charles Murphy.

JGMA is based in Chicago and was founded in 2010 by Juan Gabriel Moreno with Cosmin Vrajitoru and Jason Nuttelman. The office has built projects at all scales in North America, Latin America, Asia and the Middle East. Moreno is the past president of ARQUITECTOS (the Society of Latino Architects in Chicago).

JOHN RONAN is founding principal and lead designer of John Ronan Architects. His abstract yet sensuous work explores materiality and atmosphere. Ronan's firm has received two AIA Institute National Honor Awards, for the Poetry Foundation and the Gary Comer Youth Center, both in Chicago. In 2010, Princeton Architectural Press published *Explorations*, a monograph of his work, and a book on the Poetry Foundation by Centerline Press at the University of Texas will be released in 2015. Ronan is currently professor of architecture at the Illinois Institute of Technology College of Architecture.

JOHNSTON MARKLEE, led by principals Sharon Johnston and Mark Lee, has a diverse portfolio of built projects, such as the Hill House in Los Angeles (2004). The firm draws upon an extensive network of collaborators to expand the breadth of design research, with a particular focus on the arts. Current projects include a new building for the Menil Drawing Institute in Houston, Texas, and a forthcoming book, *House Is a House Is a House Is a House*. Johnston and Lee are teaching a multi-year studio at Harvard University's Graduate School of Design.

JUNYA.ISHIGAMI+ASSOCIATES was established by Junya Ishigami in 2004, following his experience at SANAA, and is based in Tokyo. The firm curated the Japanese Pavilion at the 2008 Venice Architecture Biennale, and won a Golden Lion for Best Project at the 2010 Biennale. Among their built projects, the Kanagawa Institute of Technology Workshop was awarded the Architectural Institute of Japan Prize in 2009. In 2014, Ishigami was Kenzo Tange Design Critic at the Harvard Graduate School of Design, and in 2015 he will be a visiting professor at Princeton University's School of Architecture.

The Berlin-based firm KÉRÉ ARCHITECTURE was founded by Burkina Faso-born architect Diébédo Francis Kéré. Using his formal training as an architect, Kéré develops strategies for innovative construction by combining traditional Burkinabé building techniques and materials with modern engineering methods. Among many other projects, Kéré built several schools in his home town of Gando, Burkina Faso, between 2001 and 2013; the primary school won the Aga Khan Award for Architecture in 2004. The firm's work has been featured in a number of exhibitions and publications.

KRUECK+SEXTON ARCHITECTS is an office in Chicago founded in 1979. Among their many built projects are the Spertus Institute for Jewish Learning and Leadership, opened in 2007, and the Crown Fountain installation in Millennium Park, completed in 2004. The studio oversaw the restoration of Mies van der Rohe's 860–880 Lake Shore Drive apartments in 2009.

KUEHN MALVEZZI was established in Berlin in 2001. Public spaces and exhibition design are the main focus of the firm's work; their built projects include the architectural design for Documenta 11, the Flick Collection in Berlin, and the Julia Stoschek Collection in Düsseldorf. Their projects have been shown in international exhibitions, including the Venice Architecture Biennale in 2006, 2012, and 2014.
 ARMIN LINKE is a photographer and filmmaker living in Milan and Berlin; among his many projects are the film *Alpi* (2004), *Il Corpo dello Stato* (at MAXXI Rome, 2010), and the *Anthropocene Observatory* (with Territorial Agency, 2014).

MARKO LULIĆ is an artist living in Vienna, whose work is concerned with the intersection of architectural modernism, ideology, and aesthetics.

LANDON BONE BAKER ARCHITECTS is a Chicago-based firm that earned a strong reputation for bringing responsible design to affordable housing and neighborhood planning. Headed by Peter Landon, Jeff Bone, Catherine Baker, the firm's growing portfolio includes small- and large-scale urban developments, affordable apartment renovations, daycare centers and college dormitories.

LATERAL OFFICE, founded by Lola Sheppard and Mason White in 2003, is an experimental design practice that operates at the intersection of architecture, landscape, and urbanism. Much of their research revolves around the Arctic. They curated the Canadian Pavilion at the 2014 Venice Architecture Biennale, *Arctic Adaptations*, which was awarded a special mention. White is associate professor at the Daniels Faculty of Architecture, Landscape, and Design at the University of Toronto, while Sheppard is associate professor at the University of Waterloo.

LCLA OFFICE, founded by Colombian architect Luis Callejas in 2011, is based in Medellín and Cambridge, Massachusetts. Completed projects include the Aquatic Center in Medellín and the El Campin soccer stadium in Bogotá. Callejas is also a faculty member at Harvard University's Graduate School of Design. Since 2014, he has been partnering with the Swedish architect Charlotte Hansson on exhibitions and spatial experiments that involve unconventional cartographies, representations, and interventions in tropical and Nordic landscapes.

LIST is a Paris-based architecture, urban planning, and research office, founded in 2012 by Ido Avissar. LIST's practice is focused on Europe and operates mainly in France, Belgium, and Switzerland. Avissar currently teaches at the École Nationale Superieure d'Architecture de Versailles, and is a visiting tutor at The Berlage in the Netherlands.

MAIO was founded in 2005 in Barcelona and is led by Maria Charneco, Alfredo Lérida, Guillermo López, and Anna Puigjaner. The studio's members combine professional activities with academic research and editorial pursuits. They are currently in charge of the magazine *Quaderns d'Arquitectura i Urbanisme* and teach at the ETSAB and ETSAV schools in Barcelona. Recently, MAIO co-curated a Weekend Special at the 2014 Venice Architecture Biennale. The studio is currently working on a range of projects, including a new housing block in Barcelona.

MAKEKA DESIGN LAB is an architecture and urban design practice in Cape Town, South Africa, established in 2002. Its principal Mokena Makeka has lectured and published extensively on topics of urban culture, African urbanism, and planning theory; Makeka has been visiting critic and lecturer at the University of Cape Town and Columbia University. The firm has received the Gold Loerie Award for Communication Design in Architecture (2011) and the CIA Merit Award for the Khayelitsha Multipurpose Centre (2009). Among several public and infrastructural commissions, the firm designed the expansion of the Cape Town train station, completed in 2010.

MARK WASIUTA teaches at GSAPP, Columbia University where he is director of exhibitions, director of Collecting Architecture Territories, and co-director of the CCCP program. He recently curated *La fine del mondo* at the 2014 Venice Architecture Biennale, and co-edited *Dan Graham's New Jersey* (Lars Müller, 2012). ADAM BANDLER is exhibitions coordinator for the Arthur Ross Architecture Gallery at GSAPP and teaches in the CCCP program. MARCOS SÁNCHEZ teaches graduate post-professional studios and seminars in the history and theory of architecture at the University of Southern California.
 The Exhibitions program at GSAPP, Columbia University, is a platform for testing and developing curatorial strategies and exhibition-related research practices, analyzing and exposing important and under-examined architectural projects and practices from the postwar period.

MASS STUDIES is a practice led by Minsuk Cho in Seoul, working on architectural projects that involve different contexts, scales, and programs. Cho is an active speaker at design and architecture symposiums worldwide and has been exhibiting his work since the late 1990s. For the Gwangju Design Biennale in 2011, directed by Seung H-Sang and Ai Weiwei, Cho co-curated *Named Design* with Anthony Fontenot. He was Commissioner of the Korean Pavilion at the 2014 Venice Architecture Biennale, winning the Golden Lion for the Best National Pavilion.

HYUN-SUK SEO interrogates space, modernity, and theatricality in his creative and academic projects. Many of his stage productions, such as *Fat Show* (2009) and *Stage Fright* (2013), are site-specific projects that incorporate the theater's interior as an integral condition of the viewing experience. Seo co-founded and co-edits *Ob.scene*, a magazine for interdisciplinary arts or "things out of the stage"; he currently teaches at Yonsei Graduate School of Communication and Arts in Seoul.

MICHAEL PECIRNO is a London-based designer whose work focuses on storytelling through visual and built experiences. His work crosses the boundaries of traditional design disciplines in order to create enriched objects, spaces, and ideas. Pecirno has been an invited research fellow and scholarship recipient at multiple institutions, including the Architectural Association in London, and Archeworks School of Design in Chicago. His work and writing have been featured in *Wired Magazine*, *Gizmodo*, *The Washington Post*, and numerous other spaces and publications.

MOON HOON spent his childhood in the mining town of Sangdongeup, in Korea, and his adolescence on the island of Tasmania, Australia. He founded his Seoul-based practice Moonbalsso in 2001; recent works include Rock It Suda, Panorama House, Ongdalsam, K-Pop Curve, and Sangsang Museum. Moon Hoon works across different genres and methods of expression, such as drawings, installations, and performances, seeking to expand the horizons of architecture. His drawings were exhibited at the 2014 Venice Architecture Biennale, and some of them are in the collection of the Tchoban Foundation in Berlin.

MOS ARCHITECTS is a New York-based collective of architects, thinkers, and designers. Principals

and co-founders Hilary Sample and Michael Meredith teach at Columbia University and Princeton University, respectively. MOS has received numerous awards for its work, including the Academy Award for Architecture from the American Academy of Arts and Letters, and a Holcim Award Silver 2014 (Asia Pacific). Recent projects include an architecture and design school in Krabbesholm, Denmark, and Chamber, a design gallery in New York.

François Roche is co-founder, together with Camille Lacadée, of NEW-TERRITORIES, a platform for research and practice that includes R&Sie(n) in Paris, Lab M4 (MindMachineMakingMyths), and [eIf/b t/c] Institute for Contingent Scenarios, Bangkok. Through these different groups, Roche seeks to articulate the passages between the real and fictional, as well as the geographic situations and narrative structures that transform that relationship. Working between architecture and film, Lacadée's primary interest is in the physical manifestation of psychopathologies, through the interactions of stage props and short films.

NIKOLAUS HIRSCH / MICHEL MÜLLER is a Frankfurt-based office for architecture. Their work on institutional models resulted in realized projects such as the Bockenheimer Depot Theater (with William Forsythe), Unitednationsplaza in Berlin (with Anton Vidokle), Cybermohalla Hub in Delhi, and Do We Dream under The Same Sky (Art Basel, 2015). They designed several exhibitions, including *Making Things Public* at ZKM (curated by Bruno Latour and Peter Weibel, 2005) and *Indian Highway* (Serpentine Gallery, 2008). Between 2010 and 2013, Nikolaus Hirsch was the director of Städelschule and Portikus in Frankfurt. Michel Müller is an architect based in Darmstadt, Germany.

NLÉ is an architecture, design, and urbanism practice founded by Kunlé Adeyemi in 2010 and based in Lagos and Amsterdam. Recent work includes the Makoko Floating School, a floating structure located on the lagoon heart of Lagos, Nigeria; this acclaimed project is part of an extensive research initiative, *African Water Cities*. Adeyemi previously worked for OMA for nearly a decade. In 2014, he was Baird Distinguished Visiting Critic at Cornell University.

NOERO ARCHITECTS was founded by Jo Noero in Johannesburg in 1984; the practice now has offices in Cape Town and Port Elizabeth as well. Noero was one of the first architects to work in the South African townships during apartheid. He believes that architecture needs to express the needs and aspirations of every woman and man in special but sometimes ordinary ways. Noero Architects has been awarded the Lubetkin Prize from RIBA, the Erskine Prize from Sweden, as well as the gold medal for architecture from the South African Institute of Architects. Noero was director of the School of Architecture and Planning at the University of Cape Town from 2000 to 2005.

NORMAN KELLEY is an architecture and design collaborative led by Thomas Kelley in Chicago and Carrie Norman based in New York and Chicago. Their work, which includes site-specific drawings, uses disruptive optics to reexamine architecture's relationship to perception. Since opening an office in 2012, Norman Kelley's work has been published and exhibited widely, most recently at the Venice Architecture Biennale in 2014, the Graham Foundation for Advanced Studies in the Fine Arts, and the American Academy in Rome. Kelley is currently assistant professor at the UIC School of Architecture, while Norman is a senior design associate with SHoP Architects in New York.

OFFICE KGDVS was founded in 2002 in Brussels by Kersten Geers and David Van Severen. It produces idiosyncratic architecture, which includes utopian and unrealized projects. The practice was awarded the Belgian Prize for Architecture in 2008, and the Silver Lion at the 2010 Venice Architecture Biennale. Geers is also a founding member and editor of *San Rocco* magazine, and frequently publishes essays on architecture in a variety of publications. Van Severen currently teaches architectural design at the Académie d'Architecture in Versailles.

BAS PRINCEN is an artist who lives and works in Rotterdam. Through his photographs, he represents the edges of the urban condition as an abstract and ambiguous space. Princen published several books, including *Refuge: Five Cities* (SUN, 2009).

ONISHIMAKI + HYAKUDAYUKI ARCHITECTS was established by Maki

Onishi and Yuki Hyakuda in Tokyo in 2008. Their work includes a weekend house in Sengataki, Japan, in 2006, the Double Helix House in Tokyo in 2011, and the Home-for-All, a project for children living in temporary housing in Higashi-Matsushima, built in 2013.

OPEN ARCHITECTURE was founded by Li Hu and Huang Wenjing in New York City; a Beijing office was established in 2006. In 2014, they completed a high school in Beijing. In recent years, OPEN's research has focused on the social and environmental problems associated with the unprecedented speed of urban development in China.

SPIRIT OF SPACE is a creative agency based in Chicago that produces architectural films.

OTHEROTHERS is a design organization based in Bondi Junction, Australia, which undertakes research, criticism, and curatorial work. Founded by architectural curator Grace Mortlock and designer David Neustein, the organization works in parallel with Other Architects, Neustein's architectural practice. Since 2011, it has produced public exhibitions, journal articles, competition entries, and unsolicited urban proposals, drawing on a diverse network of collaborators.

P-A-T-T-E-R-N-S is an architectural design practice based in Los Angeles and directed by Argentinian architects Marcelo Spina and Georgina Huljich. The office works across scales, programs, and cultures, integrating advanced technology with an extensive consideration of form, novel tectonics, and innovative materials. Spina has been on the faculty at SCI-Arc, Los Angeles, since 2001 and is coordinator of the ESTm Program in the school. Huljich is adjunct associate professor at the Department of Architecture at UCLA, and director of the Summer Program Institute.

CASEY REHM is a designer and algorithmic consultant based in Los Angeles, where he founded the studio Kinch.

PEDRO&JUANA is a studio in Mexico City run by Ana Paula Ruiz Galindo and Mecky Reuss. The studio experiments with textures, technology, craft, scale, and color; they look for feedback loops between design and fabrication, materials and construction

processes both analogue and digital. Recent works include Turin 42, an apartment complex within and on top of a 1918 house in Mexico City, a kitchenette entrance for Dorothea Schlueter Galerie in Hamburg, and the pavilion *Hotel Palenque Is Not in Yucatan* at the Hessel Museum of Art in Annandale-on-Hudson, New York.

PEDRO REYES was born in 1972 in Mexico City, where he lives and works. His work addresses the interplay between physical and social space, making tangible the invisible geometry of our personal relationships. His expanded notion of sculpture examines the cognitive contradictions of modern life, and the possibility of overcoming our particular crises by increasing our individual and collective degree of agency.

Solo exhibitions of Reyes's work took place at the Hammer Museum, Los Angeles (2014); ICA, Miami (2014); The Power Plant, Toronto (2014); Whitechapel Gallery, London (2013); Walker Art Center, Minneapolis (2011); Guggenheim Museum, New York (2011); CCA Kitakyushu, Japan (2009); Bass Museum, Miami (2008); and the San Francisco Art Institute (2008). Group exhibitions include documenta 13 (2013) and the Liverpool Biennial (2012).

PEZO VON ELLRICHSHAUSEN is an art and architecture studio established in Concepción, southern Chile, in 2002, by Mauricio Pezo and Sofia von Ellrichshausen. They regularly teach at the IIT College of Architecture in Chicago and La Pontificia Universidad Católica de Chile in Santiago. The studio's work has been featured in monographic issues of *A+U* (2013), *2G* (2012), and *ARQ* (2007) and exhibited at the 2010 Venice Architecture Biennale, and at the Royal Academy of Arts (2014).

PIOVENEFABI is a Milanese practice led by Ambra Fabi and Giovanni Piovene, specializing in architecture, urban research, and territorial visions. The office's activity develops through commissions, competitions, publications, workshops, and teaching. Giovanni Piovene was previously part of Salottobuono; Ambra Fabi is teaching at the Accademia di Architettura in Mendrisio, Switzerland.

PLAN:B ARQUITECTOS was founded in 2000 and is currently led by Felipe and Federico Mesa. Plan:b understands material practices as areas

of convergence between society and the environment. Its work is generated primarily through participation in architectural competitions and constant collaboration with other professionals. Important works include the Orquideorama for the Medellín Botanical Garden, the Flor del Campo School in Cartagena, and several primary schools in Medellín.

POINT SUPREME was founded by Greeks Konstantinos Pantazis and Marianna Rentzou, after they studied and worked in Athens, London, Rotterdam, Brussels, and Tokyo. Their urban projects were exhibited at the 2012 Venice Architecture Biennale. The office won the first prize at Europan 10 for a social housing and master plan in Trondheim, Norway, and they recently built a public space in Tel Aviv.

In 2012, Point Supreme was included by LIFO newspaper among the twenty most influential personalities in Greece.

PORT URBANISM is a design consultancy based in Chicago, and founded by Andrew Moddrell and Christopher Marcinkoski in 2010. Drawing from a collective background in contemporary urban issues, the practice specializes in new forms of collective space ranging from plazas and public waterfronts to framework plans and regional planning strategies. With projects in Denver, Los Angeles, Chicago, and Philadelphia, PORT's work has been the recipient of a number of professional awards, including an AIA Award in 2014 for the Denver Parks and Recreation City Loop project.

PRODUCTORA is a Mexico City-based firm led by architects Carlos Bedoya, Wonne Ickx, Victor Jaime, and Abel Perles. PRODUCTORA's residential, public, and corporate work has been presented in several biennials and exhibitions. The Architectural League of New York nominated the firm for the Young Architects Forum in 2007, and Emerging Voice in 2013. In 2011, PRODUCTORA founded, with curator and art critic Ruth Estévez, LIGA Space for Architecture, a gallery to promote emerging Latin-American architecture.

RAAAF (Rietveld Architecture-Art-Affordances), founded in 2006 by Ronald and Erik Rietveld, develops research and strategic interventions at the intersection of science, art, and architecture. Architect Arna Mackic joined the Rietvelds in 2009, bringing her interest in cultural heritage. Among their projects are the celebrated installation *Vacant NL* at the Venice Architecture Biennale 2010, and *Secret Operation 610*, completed in 2013.

RAMAK FAZEL is a photographer based in Italy and the US. The effect of geographic displacement and the inherent contradictions of cultural identity are themes at the heart of his cultural production. Working within, around, and sometimes against the traditions of photography and installation, he has examined the idea of the individual as a reflection of place and an expression of influences.

In 2008, Fazel exhibited the photographic essay "49 Capitols" at the Storefront for Art and Architecture in New York City. Along with photographs of the journey, the project provides a narrative of the search for an increasingly complicated idea of American identity. An installation of his ongoing project *The Business of People* was on exhibition at the Venice Architecture Biennale in 2014. Currently, he is visiting lecturer at San Francisco Art Institute.

RUA ARQUITETOS, established by Pedro Évora and Pedro Rivera in 2008 in Rio de Janeiro, explores mobile and temporary innovations in spatial design. RUA Arquitetos was awarded the design for the Rio 2016 Olympic Games Golf Clubhouse. In 2014, the firm participated in the exhibition *Uneven Growth: Tactical Urbanisms for Expanding Megacities* at the Museum of Modern Art, New York.

RURAL URBAN FRAMEWORK is the design and research collaborative of Joshua Bolchover and John Lin, established in response to the Chinese government's announcement that it planned to urbanize half of the remaining 700 million rural citizens by 2030. Hosted by the University of Hong Kong, RUF provides design services to charities and NGOs working in Chinese villages on projects such as schools, hospitals, housing, and incremental planning strategies. Their approach integrates local construction practices with contemporary technologies, in addition to in-depth social and economic research on the transformation of Chinese villages.

SANTIAGO BORJA is an artist from Mexico City. Born in 1970, his work explores convergences in art, architecture, and anthropology, with installations that juxtapose cultural objects and architectural interventions. Recent solo projects include *Sitio* at Le Corbusier's Villa Savoye, *Fort Da / Sampler* at the Neutra-VDL House in Los Angeles and *In the Shadow of the Sun* at the Irish Museum of Modern Art, Dublin. Borja has received grants from the Graham Foundation and the Fundación Marcelino Botín, among others.

SELGASCANO was founded in 1998 by Madrid natives José Selgas and Lucía Cano. By borrowing technologies from fields that are rarely joined with architecture, their projects consider the entire construction process—from manufacture to installation—to extrapolate elements of beauty. In 2015, selgascano became the first Spanish practice to design the Serpentine Pavilion in London. In 2013, they were awarded the Kunstpreis by the Akademie der Kunste in Berlin, and the Architects of the Year award by the German Design Council in Munich. Selgascano have exhibited their work at the Museum of Modern Art and the Guggenheim Museum in New York.

Mark SMOUT and Laura ALLEN work mainly on architectural competitions and on conceptual design projects at the scale of the landscape. They are lecturers at the Bartlett School of Architecture, UCL, where Smout also directs the masters program in Urban Design.

GEOFF MANAUGH is editor of the acclaimed BLDGBLOG, and previously worked for *Dwell*, *Gizmodo*, and *Wired*. He is based in Los Angeles.

SO-IL is an idea-driven design firm that brings together extensive experience from the fields of architecture, academia, and the arts; it is lead by partners Florian Idenburg, Jing Liu, and Ilias Papageorgiou. SO-IL has worked on an array of projects including the master plan of a cultural campus in Shanghai, the flagship store for United Colors of Benetton in New York City, the Frieze Art Fair in NYC, and Kukje Gallery in Seoul.

SOM (Skidmore, Owings & Merrill) is one of the world's leading architecture, engineering, urban planning, and interior design firms. Founded in Chicago nearly eighty years ago, the firm has completed more than 10,000 projects across fifty countries. Its portfolio includes some of the most important design accomplishments of the twentieth and twenty-first centuries, ranging from the plan of Chicago's Millennium Park and London's Canary Wharf to civic structures such as the Hirshhorn Museum in Washington, DC, to towers including Chicago's John Hancock Center and Willis Tower, New York's One World Trade Center, and Dubai's Burj Khalifa.

CAMESGIBSON is an architecture and design practice based in Chicago. Founded in 2009 by Grant Gibson and the fictitious T. E. Cames, the firm produces critical work that blends modern enthusiasm and postmodern irony. Grant Gibson is clinical assistant professor at the University of Illinois at Chicago School of Architecture.

SOU FUJIMOTO ARCHITECTS, established in Tokyo in 2000, is a group of architects, designers, craftsmen, and thinkers dedicated to bringing imagination to the built environment. In 2013, Sou Fujimoto became the youngest architect to design the annual summer pavilion for the Serpentine Gallery in London. In 2014, he was awarded *The Wall Street Journal*'s Architecture Innovator Award. Among his notable projects are House NA in Tokyo, completed in 2012.

STEFANO BOERI ARCHITETTI, based in Milan since 1998, is a partnership led by Stefano Boeri and Michele Brunello. An international team of about forty collaborators is working on projects across Europe, South America, and Asia. SBA has recently completed the Centre Régional de la Mediterranée in Marseilles, and the Bosco Verticale towers in Milan. Along with Richard Burdett, Jacques Herzog, and William MacDonough, Stefano Boeri has been part of the architectural team in charge of developing guidelines for the Expo 2015 in Milan. He is professor of Urban Design at Politecnico di Milano. From 2004 to 2007 he was director of *Domus*, and of *Abitare* from 2007 to 2011.

STUDIO ALBORI, established in 1992 by Emanuele Almagioni, Giacomo Borella, and Francesca Riva, works on projects paying particular attention to how energy and the environment intersect with everyday living. Recent work includes a solar-powered house and a school in the Italian Alps. The studio has participated in international exhibitions and conferences including the Venice Architecture Biennale in 2008 and 2014 and Bienal Panamericana de Quito in 2012, and has organized community workshops in Naples, Rome, and Milan.

STUDIO [D] TALE was founded by Safia Qureshi and Maxwell Mutanda. Rooted in storytelling and research, the studio experiments with architecture, product, photography, and film to discover new materials and innovations. Recent exhibitions include installations at the Louisiana Museum in Denmark and at the 2014 Venice Architecture Biennale. Their work has been published by Architecture-Studio for the program *Young Architects in Africa*.

STUDIO GANG, founded by MacArthur fellow Jeanne Gang in 1997, is based in Chicago and New York. A creative team of architects, designers, and thinkers, the Studio operates as a laboratory to identify urban patterns, test ideas and materials, and develop new models at various scales. Built projects include the Aqua Tower in Chicago, completed in 2009, and the Arcus Center for Social Justice Leadership in Kalamazoo, Michigan, finished in 2014.

TATIANA BILBAO tries to influence the cultural and economic development of space in reaction to the dehumanizing effects of global capitalism. Her work includes an open-air chapel for the Ruta del Pelegrino in Mexico (2011), and a house for artist Gabriel Orozco (2008). Bilbao's firm was the recipient of the Berliner Kunstpreis in 2012 and the Global Award for Sustainable Architecture Prize in 2013. Tatiana Bilbao is currently on the faculty at Yale School of Architecture.

TIGERMAN McCURRY ARCHITECTS was established in Chicago in 1964. Stanley Tigerman has designed hundreds of buildings and installations throughout North America, Europe and Asia; and was selected to represent the United States at the 1976, 1980, and 2012 Venice Architecture Biennale. Tigerman was a founding member of the Chicago Seven group, as well as the Chicago Architectural Club. Margaret McCurry's projects have been published and exhibited widely; she is the recipient of Honor Awards from both the AIA National and Chicago Chapters, and has given lectures at multiple conferences and schools of architecture.

TOMA is a professional collective that has operated since 2012 in Santiago de Chile. It is currently composed of five architects: Leandro Cappetto, Mathias Klenner, Eduardo Perez, Ignacio Rivas, and Ignacio Saavedra. The office develops territorial actions and research to generate alternative social ecosystems. Its production is self-managed, hands-on, and constructed with scarce resources.

Born in 1973 in Tucumán, Argentina, TOMÁS SARACENO lives and works in and beyond the planet Earth. After receiving degrees in Architecture and Art in Buenos Aires, he continued his postgraduate studies at SHBK– Städelschule, Frankfurt am Main, before going on to attend IUAV in Venice. In 2009, he took part in the International Space Studies Program at NASA and was awarded the prestigious Calder Prize. In 2012, he participated in the artistic residency at MIT Center for Art, Science & Technology, with whom he began an ongoing collaboration. Saraceno's works have been exhibited in numerous international solo and group exhibitions, such as the Metropolitan Museum of Art (2012), Hamburger Bahnhof (2011), and the Venice Art Biennale (2009). His practice, informed by the fields of art, architecture, and natural and social sciences, articulates novel and visionary statements, explores sustainable ways of sensing and inhabiting the environment, and seeks possible new relations between human, nonhuman, and the Earth.

ULTRAMODERNE is a collaboration between architects Yasmin Vobis and Aaron Forrest, and structural engineer Brett Schneider. Based in Providence, Rhode Island, and closely connected with the Rhode Island School of Design, the Ultramoderne team members bring together extensive experience in architecture, design, and engineering at a variety of scales. Vobis and Forrest have recently completed projects with the Van Alen Institute and the Boston Society of Architects, and they have extensive experience working for leading architects in San Francisco, New York, and Madrid. Schneider is senior associate at Guy Nordenson and Associates Structural Engineers in New York, where he has led projects in collaboration with SANAA, the Renzo Piano Building Workshop, Johnston Marklee, and others.

URBANLAB was cofounded by Martin Felsen and Sarah Dunn in Chicago, as a collaborative office practicing architecture and urban design. Their projects range from urban infrastructures to residential projects to architecture installations. The firm exhibited work in the Venice Architecture Biennale in 2010 and 2012, and over time has garnered several awards from the American Institute of Architects.

Matias Echanove and Rahul Srivastava are co-founders of the URBZ collective, which organizes collaborative design workshops around the world. Previous workshops took place in Tokyo, Istanbul, Mumbai, New Delhi, São Paulo, and Rio de Janeiro. They joined forces through their blog airoots/eirut in 2006 and are now co-directors of the Institute of Urbanology, with offices in Mumbai and Goa, India. They have authored essays and commentaries published by *The New York Times*, *The Wall Street Journal*, *The Hindu*, *The Times of India*, and other journals. Their work has been exhibited at the Museum of Modern Art in New York, MAK in Vienna, the Istanbul Design Biennial, and the São Paulo Cultural Center. Matias Echanove studied government and economics, and urban planning at Columbia University, and urban information systems at the University of Tokyo. Rahul Srivastava studied social and urban anthropology in Mumbai, Delhi, and Cambridge University.

VO TRONG NGHIA ARCHITECTS, founded in 2006, is an architectural practice in Vietnam with offices in Ho Chi Minh City and Hanoi; more than sixty professionals work closely on cultural, residential, and commercial projects worldwide. Vo Trong Nghia Architects experiments with light, wind, and water, and uses natural and local materials to create a contemporary design vocabulary, such as in the House for Trees (completed in 2014). Nghia is currently visiting professor at the Singapore University of Technology and Design.

WAI ARCHITECTURE THINK TANK is an international studio practicing architecture, urbanism, and architectural research, founded in Brussels in 2008 by Cruz García and Nathalie Frankowski. Currently, the studio and its parallel art practice Garcia Frankowski are based in Beijing. WAI Architecture Think Tank takes a panoramic approach to architecture, encompassing theoretical texts, artifacts, narrative architectures, buildings, and urban and cultural conditions. The studio's work ranges from the conception of intelligent buildings and master plans to the production of critical research projects and innovative publications. Recent international projects include the shortlisted design of the National Centre for Contemporary Arts (NCCA) in Moscow and the publication of *Pure Hardcore Icons: A Manifesto on Pure Form in Architecture* (Artifice Books on Architecture, 2013).

WEATHERS is a Chicago-based firm founded by architect Sean Lally. Lally is the author of the book *The Air from Other Planets: A Brief History of Architecture to Come* (Lars Müller, 2014). He is the recipient of the 2012 Prince Charitable Trusts Rome Prize from the American Academy in Rome and the winner of the 2012 Architectural League Prize for Young Architects and Designers.

WOLFF ARCHITECTS is a design studio based in Cape Town, South Africa, concerned with developing an architectural practice of consequence through the mediums of design, advocacy, research, and documentation. The office is led by husband-and-wife couple Ilze and Heinrich Wolff. Their work has been exhibited internationally, including at the Venice Architecture Biennale in 2006 and 2010, the São Paulo Biennial in 2005 and 2007, the Museum of Modern Art in New York, and the Louisiana Museum of Modern Art in Denmark.

Prior to establishing Wolff, Heinrich led Noero Wolff Architects with Jo Noero and is currently guest professor at ETH Zürich. Ilze, an architect and scholar within the fields of heritage, architectural history, and public culture, co-founded Open House Architecture.

WORKAC was founded in 2003 in New York City. In their effort to imagine future cities, principals Amale Andraos and Dan Wood appropriate productive aspects of the urban discourse to integrate architecture, landscape, and ecological systems. Recent projects include the master plan for the New Holland Island Cultural Center in St. Petersburg, Russia, and Wieden+Kennedy's New York offices.

ANT FARM was founded in 1968 by Chip Lord and Doug Michels, later joined by Curtis Schreier. Rooted in avant-garde architecture, graphic arts, and environmental design practice, their work includes inflatable projects, countercultural performances such as Media Burn (1975), and the iconic installation Cadillac Ranch in Amarillo, Texas (1974). While Ant Farm officially disbanded in 1978, Lord and Schreier continue to collaborate.

YASMEEN LARI is Pakistan's first woman architect, as well as an architectural historian, heritage conservationist, and humanitarian aid worker. She registered as an architect in 1969 and, after an acclaimed career in Pakistan, retired from architectural practice in 2000. In 1980, together with Suhail Zaheer, Lari founded the HERITAGE FOUNDATION OF PAKISTAN, which focuses on heritage management, research, and training. Since the earthquake in 2005, the Foundation has provided humanitarian aid to affected communities through the reintroduction of vernacular building techniques and sustainable practices.

# Chicago
Architecture
Biennial
2015

**Presenting Partners**
City of Chicago,
 Department of Cultural
 Affairs and Special Events
Graham Foundation
 for Advanced Studies
 in the Fine Arts

**Presenting Sponsor**
BP

**Regional Sponsor**
SC Johnson

**Exhibition Sponsors**
Bank of America
Jones Lang LaSalle
Tanya and Michael Polsky

**Education Sponsor**
J. Thomas Hurvis
 Chairman and Founder,
 Old World Industries /
 PEAK

**Official Hotel Sponsor**
Marriott

**Community Outreach
Sponsor**
ArcelorMittal

**Signature Sponsors**
American Institute
 of Architects
Chicago Architecture
 Foundation

**Supporters**
Pritzker Foundation
Alphawood Foundation
Mansueto Foundation
Joyce Foundation
Tawani Foundation

**Sponsors**
Skidmore, Owings &
 Merrill LLP
Nordic Structures
Paschen
reThink Wood
Rhode Island School
 of Design
Taft Stettinius &
 Hollister LLP
Clayco
Thornton Tomasetti
Herman Miller
Behr

**International Supporters**
Australian Consulate-
 General Chicago
French-American Curatorial
 Exchange Program
Consulate-General of the
 Netherlands
Pro Helvetia

**Presenting Media Partner**
BBC.com

**Media Partners**
Architect Magazine
The Architect's Newspaper
Architectural Record
Design Indaba
Dezeen
Icon
Metropolis
onoffice
PIN–UP

**Biennial Program Partners**
American Institute of
 Architects, Chicago Chapter
The Art Institute of Chicago
Chicago Architecture
 Foundation
Chicago International Film
 Festival
Chicago Park District
Chicago Public Library
Chicago Public Schools
Choose Chicago
Harris Theater for Music
 and Dance
Illinois Institute
 of Technology
Millennium Park Foundation
Museum of
 Contemporary Art
Rebuild Foundation
The School of the Art
 Institute of Chicago
University of Chicago
University of Illinois
 at Chicago

**Affiliate Program Partners**
6018 North
A+D Gallery
Aggregate Architectural
 History Collaborative
Alliance Francaise
ArchAgenda
Archeworks
Arts Club Chicago
Association of Architecture
 Organizations
Ballroom Projects
Center for Urban Pedagogy
The Chair of Complex
 Projects, TU Delft
Chicago Architectural Club
Chicago Artists Month
Chicago Design Museum
Chicago History Museum
Chicago Humanities Festival
Chicago Ideas Week
Chicago Infrastructure Trust
Chicago Women
 in Architecture
Clarke House Museum
Columbia College Chicago
Comfort Station
Council on Tall Buildings
 and Urban Habitat
Defibrillator Gallery
DePaul Art Museum
DePaul University
Design Evanston
The Richard H. Driehaus
 Foundation
DuSable Museum of African
 American History
Elmhurst Art Museum
Experimental Sound Studio
Expo Chicago
Farnsworth House
The Franklin
Frank Lloyd Wright Trust
Friends of Downtown
Friends of Historic Second
 Church
Gallery 400
Garfield Park Conservatory
Glass Curtain Gallery
Glessner House Museum
Global Architectural History
 Teaching Collaborative
Goethe-Institut
Great Cities Institute
Hyde Park Art Center
IFP/Chicago
Illinois Chapter of the
 National Organization
 of Minority Architects
Illinois Holocaust Museum
 & Education Center
Illinois Humanities
Instituto Cervantes
Istituto Italiano di Cultura

The Institute for Public
 Architecture
Italian American Chamber
 of Commerce
Italian Trade Agency
Jane Addams Hull-House
 Museum
Jane's WalkCHICAGO
Lampo
Landmarks Illinois
Los Arquitectos
Mana Contemporary
Manifest: A Journal of
 American Architecture
 and Urbanism
MAS Context
Metropolitan Planning
 Council
Mies Crown Hall Americas
 Prize
Mies van der Rohe Society
Museum of Contemporary
 Photography
Museum of Science and
 Industry
National Hellenic Museum
National Museum of
 Mexican Art
National Public Housing
 Museum
Northwestern University,
 Art History Department
Pecha Kucha Night Chicago
Preservation Chicago
Rhona Hoffman Gallery
RIBA-USA
Smart Museum of Art
Society of Architectural
 Historians
SOFA CHICAGO
The Temple Hoyne Buell
 Center for the Study of
 American Architecture,
 Columbia University
Threewalls
United States Artists
Van Alen Institute
Volume Gallery
Women's Architectural
 League Foundation
Writers' Theatre

# The State of the
# Art of Architecture
*Guidebook*

*Edited by*
Joseph Grima
Sarah Herda
Andrea Bagnato
Irene Sunwoo

*Copyediting*
Superscript

*Editorial Assistant*
Arièle Dionne-Krosnick

*Proofreading*
Simon Cowper

*Graphic Design*
Zak Group

*Prepress, Printing, and Binding*
Lowitz + Sons, Chicago

Published in occasion of the first Chicago Architecture Biennial, October 3, 2015 – January 3, 2016.

Chicago Architecture Biennial
chicagoarchitecturebiennial.org

ISBN 978-0-9967653-0-5

Printed in Chicago, USA